Praise for

The Living Dementia Approach

"The highlight of the book for me is the author's case-study approach to problem solving. Throughout the book, Gwendolyn tells stories and then comments on 'What Works' and 'What Doesn't Work.' One can read a story and then learn that it does not work to argue or use logic with persons with dementia. Instead, what works is employing humor, going with the flow or keeping the person busy.

"This case-study approach is invaluable. Family and professional caregivers are easily overwhelmed. I don't think many of them read books from start to finish. They do not have time. Instead, they benefit from quick, easy-to-read chapters that tell a compelling story and then summarize key points. This book can be used as caregiver resource material to enhance bedside care (or taught in the classroom) so that busy and stressed caregivers can learn at their own pace."

—David Troxel, M.P.H.
co-author of *The Best Friends Approach to Alzheimer's Care*

"The illustrations in this text have helped me not only to demonstrate a variety of the 'behaviors' that can be exhibited by persons with Alzheimer's and related dementia during their journey through this passage of their lives, but also assists me in training professional and family care partners and First Responders (Police, Fire & EMS) to 'think outside the box,' while attempting to understand, solve and deal with these difficult behaviors."

—Robert B. Schaefer
Author & Trainer
Greater Richmond, VA, Alzheimer's Association
winner 2006 Mid-Atlantic Humanitarian Service Award
Society of Former Special Agents, FBI.

"Every caregiver will breathe a sigh of relief after reading this. It's extremely practical. The case studies put the reader right 'in the room' with the person needing care, seeing the person and situation through the eyes of both the family members and professional caregivers. The book encourages communication and respect between persons with dementia and their caregivers and demonstrates simple ways to foster it. I learned many ways to make caregiving easier and more satisfying for everyone involved."

—**Pat Samples**
Speaker, Educator, Author of *Body Odyssey*

"The case studies supply strategies for managing the behaviors of the person with dementia by creating understanding of the phases through which they are passing, and fostering loving support by encouraging a positive acceptance of those phases and an appreciation of who the person is at their core. The case studies also identify tools and techniques which can be used to reach the person inside and enhance their reality.

The case studies and the accompanying interviews cover such a broad range of situations and yet establish many common themes. If I were a caregiver in any of these situations, I think I would find the recommendations of 'what works' AND 'what doesn't work' most helpful. This is a wonderful, educational, compassionate and life-affirming book."

—**Patty Smart-Abbey, B.S.W.**
Family Justice Counselor

"I certainly wish I'd had the information contained in 'The Living Dementia Approach' when I was trying to help and relate to my mother in her last years. One big stroke and a series of smaller strokes gradually eroded her mental abilities until she had to be cared for in a facility. If my sister and I, and the professional caregivers at the care home, had had the insights provided by these case studies and varied scenarios, we would have been able to help her feel more in control of her life, be more comfortable, and be able to share more of her fading memories with us."

—**Karen Muntean**
Artist of Persistence of Memory

The
LIVING DEMENTIA
Case-Study Approach ®

The
LIVING DEMENTIA
Case-Study Approach ®

**Caregivers Discover
What Works and
What Does Not**

Gwendolyn de Geest, RN, BSN, MA

Cover and interior design by Frits de Geest
Editing by Mary P. Brooke, B.Sc., Cert.PR
Printed and bound by Trafford Publishing

CruiseRespite
6066 Brantford Ave.
Burnaby, BC, Canada V5E 2R7
www.CruiseRespite.com

Note for Librarians: A cataloguing record for this book is available from Library and Archives Canada at www.collectionscanada.ca/amicus/index-e.html
ISBN 1-4251-1647-7

Printed in Victoria, BC, Canada. Printed on paper with minimum 30% recycled fibre.
Trafford's print shop runs on "green energy" from solar, wind and other environmentally-friendly
power sources.

Offices in Canada, USA, Ireland and UK

Book sales for North America and international:
Trafford Publishing, 6E–2333 Government St.,
Victoria, BC V8T 4P4 CANADA
phone 250 383 6864 (toll-free 1 888 232 4444)
fax 250 383 6804; email to orders@trafford.com
Book sales in Europe:
Trafford Publishing (UK) Limited, 9 Park End Street, 2nd Floor
Oxford, UK OX1 1HH UNITED KINGDOM
phone +44 (0)1865 722 113 (local rate 0845 230 9601)
facsimile +44 (0)1865 722 868; info.uk@trafford.com
Order online at:
trafford.com/07-0051

10 9 8 7 6 5 4 3 2

Acknowledgments

*T*hose who know me well will attest to the fact that I am not often speechless. I tend to think in paragraphs and speak in volumes. Sometimes I think that my children were delighted when their Mom had laryngitis.

However, when it comes to expressing unending thanks and gratitude to those who have supported me in writing The Living Dementia Approach, I am speechless. So many people have assisted me along the way.

I feel so blessed over the years, in my career and ongoing education, that I felt compelled to give something back that would touch the lives of caregivers—both family and professional—as well as the dear individuals they are caring for.

The Living Dementia Approach would never have emerged without the support, pushing, prodding and encouragement of my husband Frits who listened to my tears and heard the click of my fingers on the computer keyboard late into the night, many nights. Frits never once gave up on me; neither would he allow me to give up on myself. When I said, "No," he said, "Yes." When I said, "It can't be done," he said, "We'll do it a different way."

Many people have contributed to this book without even knowing it. They are the family and professional caregivers who have tirelessly offered tender support, care and respect for this challenged population of persons with Alzheimer's disease and related dementia. Some of these special people include Jenny, Frank, Jack, Margaret, Jean, Peggy, Alma, Susan, Joe, Ruby, Lily, and Jessica. These are only some of the unsung heroes.

I would particularly like to thank all of the kind, patient souls who took the time to look at the Reader's Edition of The Living Dementia Approach and to give me feedback: David Troxel, Karen Muntean, Patty Smart–Abbey, Robert B. Schaefer, and Pat Samples. Their guiding words of wisdom proved invaluable in the process of transforming my manuscript into a book.

I would also like to thank Karen Muntean for generously sharing her inspirational work of art, "Persistence of Memory." Through the eyes of her mother, Dorothy, I now understand the paradox of memory. The person with dementia lives totally in the moment and although caregivers of persons with dementia must embrace this person's "new reality," they also must understand that life can go on without previous memory. I personally have a great attachment to my memories. However, one can still be someone without memory. Thank you, Dorothy.

And I wish to thank one very special person, who always encourages and supports me, my dear friend of over fifty years, Patty Smart Abbey, who offers listening energy for my stories, even when her ears are tired.

I remain eternally grateful to my children Heather and Oliver, and my husband Frits, for their ongoing love and support. Even when I was at the laptop (and not in the kitchen cooking dinner) they all seemed to survive and love me anyway.

Finally, this book would never have happened if not for the sacrifices my Mother and Daddy made for me. Although Daddy has since passed, Mother remains the anchor in the family. Thank you Evelyn and John. I dedicate The Living Dementia Approach to you.

Contents

Foreword

I first met Gwendolyn at a conference in Washington State. Most of the conference participants were family caregivers hungry for information, seeking support, anxious about the future, and looking for an encouraging word. When Gwendolyn stood up to present her ideas about The Circle of Care, you could just see the connections being made. Gwendolyn understands how Alzheimer's disease and dementia impacts the person with the disease, as well as their carers. She understands what professionals and family members should do to help. And she knows what it takes to help a person with dementia feel safe, secure and valued.

In this valuable and thought provoking book, Gwendolyn describes her Dementia Care Model. This model guides individuals through the emotional phases of the journey from turmoil to trust. During this journey a strength-based approach, accompanied by creative solutions, is revealed.

I appreciate Gwendolyn's highlighting the importance of biography and life story. Persons with dementia begin to lose this; they forget names, relationships and their own past. Still, they retain a sense of self. Gwendolyn encourages us to explore who the person was before the dementia. If he or she was once cheerful and optimistic but is now sad and suspicious, we should strive to create an environment that will bring back their best qualities. With Gwendolyn's book, family and professional caregivers will learn just how to do this.

The highlight of the book for me is the author's case-study approach to problem solving. Throughout the book, Gwendolyn tells stories and then comments on "What Works" and "What Doesn't Work." One can read a story and then learn that it does not work to argue or use logic with persons with dementia. Instead, what works is employing humor, going with the flow or keeping the person busy.

This case-study approach is invaluable. Family and professional caregivers are easily overwhelmed. I don't think many of them read books from start to finish. They do not have time. Instead, they benefit from quick, easy-to-read, chapters that tell a compelling story and then summarize key points. This book can be used as caregiver resource material to enhance bedside care (or taught in the classroom) so that busy and stressed caregivers can learn at their own pace.

While reading Gwendolyn's book, I felt like I was at a stimulating support group meeting. I enjoyed and learned from the many family stories in the book, and distilled lessons from each one.

The book concludes with a series of case studies that the reader can use for applied learning. These will be particularly valuable for staff training but have utility for all of us. Gwendolyn presents a problem or situation, and then encourages us to put the principles in the book to work and list some potential steps for success.

As a writer and long-term care consultant who has worked in the field for over 20 years, I welcome Gwendolyn de Geest's contribution to our field. As a son with a beloved mother with Alzheimer's disease, I can also say that the book's kindness, creativity, and sensibility inspires me to travel the journey with my mother, to support her dignity and to focus less on the loss, and more on the moments of joy.

—David Troxel, M.P.H.
Co-Author,
The Best Friends Approach to Alzheimer's Care

Phases of the Dementia Journey

Preface

For over two decades, I have witnessed the joys and sorrows of family and professional caregivers struggling to understand the reality of loved ones or persons who have dementia. This moved me to write The Living Dementia Approach that you are reading now.

There are more than 78 million baby boomers, many of whom may find themselves being the primary caregivers of their aging parents in coming years. These individuals may not even realize that they require education and support until there is a crisis. This book is for them, as well as for professional caregivers who work with dementia sufferers and their families.

What is so different about the Living Dementia Approach to reach these family and professional caregivers? In reaching both families and professional caregivers, The Living Dementia Approach speaks through the eyes of the front-line practitioner. As a front-line practitioner myself, I see family caregivers struggling as they watch loved ones slowly slipping away, feeling helpless to prevent the inevitable loss of mind and person. I have been at many a dementia person's bedside. I have worked directly with caregivers in three different roles: supervising students and caregivers in training, guiding professional and family caregivers, and delivering hands-on care. What I experienced and learned through this direct relationship with dementia moved me to write this book.

There already exists a plentitude of excellent literature and helpful resources on the topic of dementia care. The guidelines and support in this book are intended to work in harmony with other available resources providing options in care.

In these pages you will see the many faces of dementia (including Alzheimer's disease). These many views will spark some awareness about the need for the application of creative solutions in dementia care. The creative solutions offered in the interviews and analysis following each shared-lived experience are tried and true. And they really work!

I feel that The Living Dementia Approach is a breakthrough resource for family and professional caregivers. I invite you to use this resource as a way to understand and attach meaning to the phases of the dementia journey. Using a case-study approach (see Glossary), the information in this book supports caregivers who seek to use strength-based care for the person with dementia.

With insight and clarity, this book explores common issues that caregivers face on a daily basis. From memory loss and communication challenges to the personal practicalities of bathing and wandering, this book brings the challenges of such situations to light. Using strength-based care, caregivers are better able to embrace who the person was prior to the diagnosis. This leads to better care for the person with dementia, as well as a more effective working experience for the caregiver.

In speaking directly to both family and professional caregivers, this book describes the passage through the emotional journey of dementia care. Caregivers are offered a compass by which to navigate four distinct phases of the dementia journey: Turmoil, Transformation, Transition, and Trust. This process attaches meaning to the dementia journey, empowering both the caregiver and the person with dementia by presenting situations and suggesting ways of dealing with them.

For example, a daughter reports, "When I take Dad for his doctor's appointment, it's hard to motivate him to get in the car. And when we do arrive, it's a struggle to get him out of the car. How long is this going to last?"

The Living Dementia Approach will assist such families in understanding what is going on within the dementia journey. As you read, together we will focus on the people involved in the situation of this illness, rather than on the difficulties of dementia (and in many cases, more specifically, Alzheimer's disease). Using strength-based care, caregivers will embrace who the person was prior to the diagnosis. This book reveals the many faces of care for people who are returning to the more basic self as their adult memory capacity diminishes.

In connecting theory to practice, educators will find The Living Dementia Approach useful for developing appropriate and creative care solutions for use in a variety of settings, including hospitals, care facilities, academic environments, Alzheimer's support groups, and adult day care situations.

The Living Dementia Approach offers easy-to-use tools for caring for people with dementia. A husband reports, "My wife, Rose, is in the bedroom, screaming and hissing at me." At this moment, this husband does not need scientific data about the broken brain. He needs an effective technique to care for his wife in the moment. Scientific information is always available later when there is adequate time for web searches and consultation with medical experts. The Living Dementia Approach offers basic concepts and easy-to-use tools for family and professionals who are charged with caring for people with dementia.

It's preferable to receive information as soon as possible about management of persons with dementia, rather than after situations have become difficult. As a resource for all family members and professional caregivers of persons with dementia, The Living Dementia Approach provides ideas and backup for those who now participate in a mission to care for persons with Alzheimer's disease and related dementias.

Introduction

Peggy is sitting in the restaurant having lunch with her husband, Howard. But Howard's not there.

They order their lunch: minestrone soup (Howard's favorite), caesar salad, a nice panini bread, and tea.

Howard excused himself, saying, "I have to go to the bathroom, dear."

"All right," Peggy responded. The soup came. She did not want to start without Howard, but she was hungry. Peggy finished her soup; still no sign of her husband. The salads arrived; still no Howard. The food items begin to take on secondary importance.

By now, Peggy is beginning to wonder. She asked the waiter to please check on her husband. "He's been in the men's room for a very long time," she said.

The young man complied, reporting back to Peggy, "Your

husband says to tell you that he has to wait for his friend. In fact, the two of them are engaged in conversation."

"I don't understand," Peggy said. "Howard went to the bathroom alone."

It's puzzling at this point, but we will soon find out what happens (see Chapter 5). The point is that the recognition of dementia in a friend or loved one may start like that—an odd situation that gives you a feeling of "something wrong" but it seems like a minor thing, so you possibly dismiss it.

While there are many theoretical causes of Alzheimer's disease, so far the full cause has not been determined. There is no known cure. In 1906, Dr. Alois Alzheimer cared for and documented evidence on Auguste D., a 51-year-old woman in Frankfurt, Germany. Even he did not know with certainty the cause of her illness until after her death. When he examined a slice of tissue from the woman's brain under a microscope, Dr. Alzheimer identified the plaques and tangles surrounding the neurons that are now the hallmark evidence of the Alzheimer's disease process. This was the first step in approaching a cure. While the clues to a correct diagnosis of Alzheimer's are fairly clear today, still in some situations, families do not know for sure that their loved one has suffered from Alzheimer's disease specifically, until after their death when an autopsy reveals the final truth.

Other than the comfort of suspecting the disease by name and learning about its stages of progression, Alzheimer's is heavy-going for family members and friends caring for a loved one who suffers with the disease. Understanding this situation takes courage. In order to begin alleviating the chaos and confusion that comes with caring for a person with Alzheimer's, one needs to equip themselves with information. As family caregivers attempt to deal with the activities of daily living for both their loved one, and themselves, some form of normalcy to everyday life can be restored.

When I first met Peggy, it was evident that she had more questions about Alzheimer's disease in relation to Howard's behavior than I was able to answer. In fact, Peggy and her family did not understand what was happening to the Howard they once knew. Some of their questions included: Where are we in this dementia journey? What's going on? How long does each phase last? How will I know when we are moving into the next phase? What outcomes can I expect? What information do I need?

With these and many other questions whirring in my head, I ultimately found myself as a professional dementia caregiver sitting at my empty computer screen, pondering how to assist such families. How could I possibly help them understand their journey and restore some form of normalcy to their lives? With more than two decades of experiential knowledge in dementia care, I felt I should be able to help people like Peggy and her family.

What I did not realize was that I was about to be swept away on a journey of discovery—one that I could not possibly prepare or pack for. This dementia care journey would carry me to opposite shores where these dementia answers lay woven in the tapestry of a newly painted canvas of understanding and approach.

The only thing between us is this black line: a thread thrown onto the empty page, into the empty air.

The Dementia Journey

Whose reality is this?

Some months later, I found myself standing in an artist's studio on one of the Gulf Islands in beautiful British Columbia, Canada. In this small one-room cabin studio the artist was sitting quietly in a corner, reading a book, her canvas on an easel in the center of the room.

My husband was waiting outside enjoying the natural habit of the west-coast island. Although he's a dear and does his very best to understand my work, at this moment my husband could not see any connection between this artist's studio and my work in dementia care.

As I stared at the artist's canvas, I was totally mesmerized by a black line that had been painted down the centre, not understanding the meaning of the line. Why was I moved by this art? In the painting was the image of a young girl wearing some sort of costume and she was holding up her right arm as though to give direction or permission to the viewer.

I was yet to see that this black line would indirectly assist Peggy and other families who are making the dementia journey. Understanding the meaning of this black line—a stopping point with a new reality on the other side—would serve to guide me in helping dementia caregivers to understand the distinction between the dementia-sufferer's journey and the caregiver's reality.

As the artist, Karen, approached me, she sensed my anticipatory excitement about the piece.

"Can I help you?" Karen asked.

"I don't know too much about art, but I am fascinated by this piece. Can you tell me a little bit about it?" I responded.

Karen began to share her story:

"I call this painting Persistence of Memory. The child is Dorothy, who is 14 here, wearing a Mayday costume in the Mayday parade."

Dorothy's life story unfolded: "Dorothy is 21 when she is teaching school at the Indian agency school, 23 when she marries, 62 when her husband dies. Dorothy is 83 when found hiding from the Indians, under the bed of the nursing home where she now lives, suffering from a crippling dementia.

"Apparently some aspects of Dorothy's memory are crystal clear, and at other times her memory function is blurry. Dorothy was born to a Swedish father and a German mother; they were wheat farmers in Northern Idaho, and they farmed the land that they leased from the native people in the region. For Dorothy's parents, Dorothy, and her sister Lois, life was busy and full. She apparently credited her mom and dad for doing the best they could during the economic depression of the early 1930s. When Dorothy was going to university during the depression, she had to live with some relatives and do work for them just to get by.

"Dorothy taught school for several years at the Indian

agency school near her parent's farm. Dorothy's husband was also a school teacher; he'd been in the Navy during WWII, stationed in the US. After the war they managed an office supply business, which they were eventually able to purchase.

"In their younger years how they had loved the outdoors! They enjoyed cross-country skiing together, Dorothy enjoyed her gardening, and her husband helped her with the tree pruning. They enjoyed family vacations; Dorothy liked the really nice hotels, you know, the ones with the fancy little soaps. Her husband preferred camping and fishing on vacation. After he died, the adjustment for Dorothy was difficult. She began to isolate herself and started having a series of small strokes, and eventually developed a crippling dementia.

"Now you may be wondering why I am even telling you this long story. I am the artist of Persistence of Memory. I never really knew Dorothy as a person. I only knew Dorothy as my mom. As a child growing up, I didn't always know what she was thinking or how she was feeling. She was never very emotionally open."

"What is the significance of the black line that you have presented down the centre of Persistence of Memory?" I asked Karen, recalling a passage from Margaret Atwood's The Blind Assassin (2001):

> "The only thing between us is this black line: a thread thrown onto the empty page, into the empty air."

Karen continued, "Even as a child, I felt as though there was always something missing between Mum and I. But I still need to understand who Mum is. The caregivers at the nursing home need to understand why Dorothy is hiding under the bed. And Dorothy herself needs to be cared for and understood."

The 4–T Dementia Care Model®: *Phases of the Dementia Journey*

Phase	Characteristics	Impact on Person with Dementia	Impact on Caregiver
Turmoil	• Chaos • Confusion	• Easily agitated • Time runs differently	• Does not understand • Relationship issues
Transformation	• Change in state and form	• Give up attachments • Feels, without ego	• Change in thinking • Liberation
Transition	• Move from one place to another	• Cannot remember • Anxiety increases	• When is the right time to move
Trust	• Commit, place in one's care or keeping	• Lives in the moment	• Trust that personhood is intact

I responded to Karen, "Thank you so much for sharing your story with me. I am intrigued both by your artistic work and your mother's life story. I work in dementia care, and what we see happening today is that there is one journey through dementia. However, the caregivers, both family and professional, are not on the same pathway as the person with dementia. While the caregiver, such as you reading this book, may be walking physically right beside the person, the person with dementia has his or her own inner reality. The black thread that you have illustrated in Persistence of Memory may be all that is separating these two realities. It's a simple visual statement but it represents something very broad."

I thanked Karen again and left her art studio, head bowed, eyes closed, deep with my thoughts about Persistence of Memory. Thoughts of how a simple barrier to understanding (the black line) is all that separates the caregiver from the person with dementia. Memories are personal and does it matter if they are retained later in life? Can we live effectively and happily without a full memory? Can we still be someone without our overall memory function or our specific life memories intact?

Later that month, I returned to my blank computer screen to begin developing this book, which is intended to present a philosophy of care that can help caregivers understand the dementia journey.

This approach to dementia care will help to restore some normalcy for families like Peggy and Howard, and Karen and her mother, Dorothy. Focusing on the person with dementia, using practical and compassionate solutions goes a long way in support of the person with dementia and their family. The Living Dementia Approach focuses on the richness of who this person was prior to the diagnosis of dementia rather than dwelling on the chaos and confusion that this disease contributes to the lives of all concerned.

The black thread in Persistence of Memory remained clear in my mind's eye as I began to envision what I've called "The 4–T Dementia Care Model®." This model outlines a philosophy of dementia care to help families navigate the four phases of dementia: Turmoil, Transformation, Transition, and Trust.

This philosophy of care lifts the disease and places a strong focus on the journey of the person with dementia and their family.

Turmoil discusses the early phase of the journey; it is a time of extreme confusion and chaos in the long journey of dementia. The person with dementia may become easily agitated, because they do not understand what is happening. Time is perceived differently for the person with dementia. The shared family experiences and interviews of the section about Turmoil will assist other caregivers in navigating this journey.

Transformation is about when "the caterpillar becomes the butterfly." In this phase, families feel liberated when they join the person with dementia in their journey. Dementia has a way of softening the person. There is no longer a fully functioning ego where the person's need to satisfy the "I" has faded away. Attachment to material things diminishes and the person with dementia has become transformed. As the family realizes that their loved one is living in the moment, their thinking changes about who this person "was" and are not so intense about maintaining their own reality in the situation. Once this new awareness has really taken hold, the family often feels liberated.

Transition is a time of passage from one state or place to another. At an earlier time, promises may have been made, "No Dad, we would never move you to a nursing home. We'll always care for you at home." For many families, it can prove to be a very difficult decision to find themselves breaking this promise.

In this phase of the journey, there is a transition in thinking for the family members. They realize that "Dad is trying to tell us something" and may feel (though not yet believe) that "I think things are going to be alright."

Trust is the key aspect of the fourth phase. Family members trust that the professional caregivers are adequately caring for their loved one. They may recognize the need for change in care, and will have the confidence to partner with the professional caregiver.

A daughter reports, "When I walk out the door, I trust that the professional will become an extension of my right arm in caring for Mother." On the other hand, professional caregivers trust that the family will share valuable biographical information with them so they can do their jobs properly. And, naturally, whether or not the person with dementia is fully aware of their situation, he or she trusts that care and understanding will be provided.

The person with dementia is "down to the very basics." These individuals live in the moment; receiving care and understanding makes them happy. Enjoying a chocolate ice cream cone makes them happy. And although this person may no longer have all of their memories, the family must trust that their loved one's "personhood" remains intact.

What is interesting about these phases of the dementia journey, as illustrated in many of the case studies, is that there may be an overlap during this Trust phase—a shift of the person from one phase to the next—and perhaps even a regression to an earlier phase. For example, the reader will note in the "Where is Harry" case study (Chapter 13), that although this family is in the phase of Transition, the person with dementing illness has become transformed in physical state and state of mind. Jean, the wife, changed her thinking about who her husband is, but some days, she will find herself back in the phase of Turmoil, when Harry no longer recognizes her.

Naturally, one cannot place human beings in "boxes." Each individual is unique and navigates through the journey when the time is right for them. Although it may be difficult to predict the duration of each phase, the person with dementia generally will provide some fairly evident clues that one phase is changing and that the next phase is emerging.

Even as this progression is happening, the individual may experience a relapse to a previous phase at any time. Caregivers

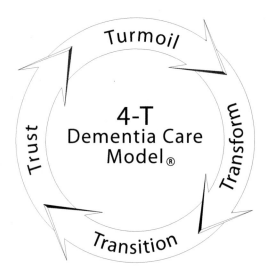

find themselves constantly playing "catch-up" to this new reality. This dynamic process is illustrated in the following 4–T Dementia Care Model®.

This book celebrates the spirit of the person who was, and aims to help family, friends and professional caregivers in the process of valuing and honoring the person who remains—the person who needs their care.

Phase 1

Turmoil

I don't understand my journey

*F*amily members have an attachment to their own reality. The person with dementia may be living in their own moment and may be wondering, "Who am I?" In this phase of the journey, everybody seems to be looking for someone. Everybody is trying to find a different place. "Where is home?"

There may even be a little conspiracy going on as the person strives to conceal that anything is the matter. Short term memory lapses, and repetition of phrases and sentences, are simply put down to being a result of "My parents are getting older," or "I'm sure Dad is fine."

This is a time of extreme confusion and chaos that comes at the onset of dementia. The person with dementia may become easily agitated, because they do not understand what is happening. "Why can't I remember?" Family members do not understand what is happening. They struggle with the fact that they no longer seem to know their loved one; this person they may have lived with for over 50 years is now behaving like a stranger.

Relationships become challenged due to a reliance on memory for the continuation of meaningful relations. We are attached to our memories; in many ways our memories and our emotional relationships define us. As the person with dementia "fades into their past," specific memories of the past 50 years are fading as well. Daughters take on a new role as a friend. The husband may become the son, the son the husband. Whose reality is this? And how can family members possibly understand the journey?

This section about the Turmoil phase will assist family and professional caregivers in understanding this phase of the journey. First, the true story will be revealed of the shared lived experience. Then an interview with the caregiver will help identify creative coping strategies. An analysis of the situation is then presented which aims to empower both the caregiver and the person with dementia. Caregivers will discover what works (and what does not) for each unique situation.

1

Reconstructing Harry

*this spouse uses bagpipes to find her husband
once again*

*J*ean and Harry have been married for over 57 years. When Harry was diagnosed with Alzheimer's disease, Jean cared for him at home as long as she could. When Harry's care became overwhelming for Jean, he was admitted to the nursing home where she visited every day, sometimes twice daily. She would assist with mealtime or take Harry for a walk. Some days when she arrived, Harry would be holding hands with another female resident. Harry no longer recognized or responded to Jean. One can well imagine the sense of loss and despair that Jean might feel at this time.

However, Jean was a real "spunky" gal. One day she had an inspiration; she thought, "I still know my Harry best, and I know that Harry is still in there." Harry had always been a "piper" in the local band and had played the bagpipes for many years. Since his Alzheimer's diagnosis, the bagpipes had been sitting in the corner gathering dust. Jean thought to herself, "I'm going to bring those bagpipes to the nursing home, just for fun, and see if Harry still recognizes them." At first Harry just looked on, not quite understanding. Eventually, a few days later, Harry picked up the bagpipes and even in late-stage dementia, he was able to play them. He would sit in the corner of the lounge, entertaining the other residents and the staff at the nursing home. The caregivers could not believe this was the same Harry they had been caring for.

Jean sat back in satisfaction and to herself spoke softly, "Yes, I've got my Harry back once again."

The interview with Jean (the wife) follows:

1   **How are things going?**

It's a confusing time for all of us. Some days Harry doesn't know me at all. I'm not sure if it matters if I visit or not. Yesterday he didn't know I was his wife; he thought I was his sister. Yet today, when our daughter visited, she said afterward, "Daddy was his old self Mom; in fact, he talked to me about when he accompanied us on a school field trip. And that was many years ago." Then there are other days when Harry becomes agitated if I ask him even the smallest question.

2   **How do you suppose you could improve the situation?**

I am learning to let go of the stuff that doesn't matter. I imagine Harry gets agitated because he can't remember many things and he doesn't understand what is going on. Yesterday, following my visit with my husband, he got really angry with the girls and said he wanted to go home. Maybe we should plan to take Harry home for a visit.

3   **What is your sense of how well this will work?**

It will be good for Harry to see his familiar things once again. And the children would really enjoy seeing their Dad at home; sometimes they are reluctant to visit him at the nursing home. I suppose that's normal.

I am a wee bit concerned though, about how we will get Harry to return to the nursing home at the end of a visit back at home.

4   **What are some possible solutions?**

I suppose I could ask the caregivers for some suggestions. One of the other family members takes her mother home every Sunday for dinner; I'm going to speak to her as well about some ideas. And our son is very good with his Dad. I'm sure he will be able to persuade Harry to get into the car.

5   **How would you describe Harry when he started playing the bagpipes once again?**

Oh, it was amazing. It was much more than just the music—I felt in that moment as though I had Harry back once again. There have been so many losses of personality and ability with this Alzheimer's disease, and so many changes in Harry. But I truly believe that Harry's spirit is alive and well in there. And we can still reach Harry on the feeling level. When Harry was playing his bagpipes, I felt like everything was going to be alright.

6   **Where do you go from here?**

I haven't worked it all out yet. I am struggling. I take one day at a time, but I do know I'll always be here for Harry. He's so vulnerable right now. I love him and I always will.

7   **What are the strengths and gaps of your present situation with Harry?**

First, the gap. My relationship and my friendship with Harry is so different now. That's because—even though I know better now—I am still holding Harry to the expectation of who he was before he deteriorated with dementia. I feel bad for both of us and for everything. Some days I am so lonely, and I cry a lot. Some days Harry recognizes me and some days he doesn't. I think I will continue to struggle with that.

Anyway, I've cried enough. This disease is not about me. Okay, here are the strengths of the situation: I know Harry is being well cared for; he is content living in the moment and he seems to enjoy the company of the others at the nursing home. And I can still reach Harry on an emotional level—we can be happy sitting together, holding hands.

8   **Sounds like Harry is being well cared for. What are some ways you care for yourself?**

Good question. I keep a close connection with a very good friend. She's a real "kindred spirit," and we are able to discuss just about anything. Although Alzheimer's has changed Harry so much, she accepts him exactly the way he is now. This helps so much, for me to see my loved one through the eyes of a supportive friend.

Also, I walk every day, and I love my garden. I find it extremely healing to work my fingers through the soil and talk to my plants.

9   **What have you learned about caring for Harry?**

I've learned that life goes on in spite of the Alzheimer's disease. I've learned to let go of some of my attachment to reality. I've learned that sometimes Harry will try to cover up his memory loss when he can't remember something. And that's when he gets agitated. So, I just go with the flow and change the subject. Then we both laugh about it.

Analysis

This story illustrates the importance of recognizing the personhood of the individual with dementia. In other words, who was Harry before the diagnosis of Alzheimer's disease? Family caregivers like Jean play a vital role in assisting the professional caregiver to embrace Harry as a person. Jean knows Harry best. She knows who Harry is. She has biographical information about Harry that professionals will find helpful in order to provide better care.

In the Turmoil phase, family members struggle with the fact that they no longer know their loved one as they once were. Harry does not function as the same person Jean has lived with for over 50 years. Jean can now expect challenging behaviors from Harry. She can expect that there will be communication difficulties when her husband is no longer able to express exactly what he wants to say. However, there will also be moments when Harry is mostly alert.

When relationships become an issue—when a wife becomes the sister, and daughters or sons must take on new unexpected roles—families need assistance and support in understanding the journey. Alzheimer's disease has changed the dynamics of the family. Jean and her children wish it was not so, but they are still standing and surviving. And so is Harry.

What Works
- Understand Harry's reality
- Focus on Harry's strengths
- Modify Harry's environment
- Reminisce about good times

What Doesn't Work
- Attachment to who Harry was
- Logical reasoning
- Unrealistic expectations

2

Wheelchair Ballet

this ballet is not for dancing

*T*he video camera on the wall of Swan Lake Manor is recording. All the film sees is a lone person, Lydia, sitting in a wheelchair in the long corridor. Her shoulders are hunched and her head is covered with a brightly colored scarf.

This camera is meant to see all. And, this early Saturday morning, it did.

The clock on the wall says 7:31 a.m. Screams are heard echoing down the long hall way of Swan Lake Manor.

"Help me, help me!" screams Lydia, as she inches her wheelchair painfully, slowly forward.

No response. The camera does not pick up anyone or anything joining the drama.

"Nurse, nurse, nurse!" The screams are becoming shrieks now. Still no response.

However, at approximately 7:37 a.m., a caregiver is seen

dashing across the hallway, pausing to contemplate the screams of help and then marching on.

Soon, a resident named Alfred waltzes in a wheelchair around the corner.

"What's all the screaming about?" Alfred asks Lydia, moving his wheelchair closer to her.

"Help, help, help!" Lydia continues, as she pushes her wheelchair along, ignoring Alfred.

"Oh shut up!" Alfred shouts, extending his right foot and giving Lydia's wheelchair a good, sound kick. A dead-eyed stare shoots back from Lydia.

It is now 7:49 a.m., and there is no one in sight.

By 7:51 a.m., the screaming continues, and Alfred has had enough. He dances his wheelchair over to the nursing unit of Swan Lake Manor, and says to the nurse, "Can't you hear Lydia making all that racket down the hall? Why don't you do something about it? It's driving us all crazy."

The nurse is consumed with her work at the nurse's station, barely glancing up. She calmly replies, "Oh, that's just Lydia telling us she wants us to push her wheelchair to the dining room for breakfast. She's always like that Alfred, don't worry."

The shouts for help are still heard down the long, empty corridor,

"Help, help, help me!" shouts Lydia. The clock goes on ticking at Swan Lake Manor; it is now 8:06 a.m. and breakfast will be served at 9:00 a.m.

The interview with Lydia's nurse follows:

1   **What message do you think Lydia is trying to deliver? And why do you think she repeats herself so much?**

I guess she might be telling us she is hungry. Or maybe she is lonely and wants the girls to give her some attention.

It's just that everyone is so busy early in the morning getting everyone ready for breakfast, that nobody has time to spend with Lydia.

I don't think Lydia remembers when we tell her that breakfast is coming, or that we will help her when we can. She just keeps screaming.

2 **Why do you suppose Lydia keeps screaming?**

I imagine this is because of Lydia's mental deterioration. She really is doing the best she can. I'm thinking maybe Lydia can't understand what's going on and she is afraid.

3 **Does she know where she is living? And does she know when and where breakfast is being served?**

Some days, Lydia thinks she is still living in Russia where she was born. It seems no matter how many times the girls tell her she is now living at Swan Lake Manor, she doesn't remember. The same thing happens with meal times. Even after Lydia has finished her breakfast, she will ask the girls, "Is it breakfast time yet?"

4 **This must be very frustrating for you and your staff.**

Absolutely. The girls have been caring for Lydia for a long time and they are used to her behavior. Although it may appear that we have been ignoring Lydia this morning, we have to put up with this on a daily basis. And, we do have 75 residents to prepare for their breakfast time.

5 **Do you have some suggestions as to how caregivers can focus on Lydia's remaining skills?**

That's a really good question. Lydia has always enjoyed cooking, gardening and classical music. Also, she loves being around small children. I intend to speak with her daughter and find out some more information about Lydia.

6   **What might be some ways of maintaining Lydia's respect and dignity in this situation?**

Now that you mention it, perhaps we could bring Lydia to the dining room earlier, and she could assist the girls in the kitchen. Or, maybe we could even turn on some classical music for her, while she is waiting for breakfast. Sometimes she seems comforted and reassured by listening to a tape of a family member's voice.

7   **Do you see any benefits in leaving Lydia in bed a little longer in the morning?**

That might just work. The girls could turn on her music by the bedside and Lydia could rest until closer to breakfast time. But some days, as soon as she wakes up, she wants to get up. Just like the rest of us, I guess.

8   **Anything else you want to add?**

Yes, I have noticed that Lydia communicates with feelings, more than with words. If we take the time to sit with Lydia, it helps us so much more to understand the person inside.

Also, I am going to speak with the girls in the kitchen. If Lydia is up early, perhaps she can help with some of the early morning preparation for breakfast time, such as setting the table.

Analysis

The person with dementia lives in their own moment. Lydia has her own reality, and is operating from a different mental place than her caregivers. She may become easily agitated when she realizes she needs to remember something or someone.

"How come I can't remember?" Lydia suffers from short-term memory lapses, which is why she repeats herself over and over again. She cannot remember from one minute to the next what she has said or not said.

This is a time of extreme confusion and chaos in the dementia journey. Both professional and family caregivers struggle with the fact that the person with dementia seems to have a different reality. Relationships become an issue. Even Lydia's daughter has taken on a new role as her friend. Time is running differently for Lydia. She is in a muddled period. In fact, Lydia cannot remember whether or not she has eaten breakfast.

We are all attached to our memories. Memories define who we are. Lydia may be recalling memories from long ago when she was preparing breakfast for her family in Russia. Now she is living in a care home. As Lydia "fades into her past," the memory of the past 50 years may fade as well. The paradox of memory remains. In other words, can life still go on without memory? And how can caregivers possibly understand Lydia's reality?

What Works
- Family shares biographical information with professional caregiver
- Spending one-on-one time with Lydia
- Joining Lydia on her journey

What Doesn't work
- Logical reasoning
- Social isolation
- Preventing Lydia from exploring

3

One Shoe On

this person with dementia is looking for yesterday

*B*ob is a resident at Memory Care Manor. Bob cannot remember how he got here, or even why he lives here. He is in middle-stage Alzheimer's disease. Most days, Bob wanders the hallways of the care centre, not recognizing the caregivers or the other residents. Some days Bob has no memory of his wife, Margaret, or his family.

This morning, Bob has only one shoe on and he is aimlessly pushing the linen cart down the hall. The nurse attempts to move the cart back to its position; however, Bob resumes his task of pushing the linen cart. A short time later, Bob is seen pushing one of the residents, Marjorie, in her wheelchair into the dining room. This upsets Marjorie a great deal. Loud screams are heard from the dining room.

"Let me go, let me go!" says Marjorie from her wheelchair.

When Bob sits down to eat his breakfast, he takes only two mouthfuls of the cereal, then rises to leave the table, resuming his wandering pattern. When he sits down in the lounge, Bob sits for a short time, then he moves to the next chair for an equally short time. The caregivers cannot encourage Bob to finish his breakfast.

Bob's wife arrives for a visit this morning. Margaret and Bob have been married for over 50 years, and she cared for Bob at home for three years prior to his admission to Memory Care Manor. This morning Margaret has found Bob's one shoe that he left behind in one of the other resident's rooms when he was wandering.

"Good morning Bob," she greets her husband with a kiss and a smile. Bob recognizes her and smiles.

The nurse tells Margaret that Bob has been pushing the linen carts and wheelchairs around the unit this morning and causing some of the residents to be upset. She says this right in front of Bob.

Margaret replies, "I feel that if Bob is not hurting himself or anyone else that the behavior should be allowed."

Bob now sits in the chair, with rounded shoulders, eyes downcast, fists tight. He is no longer responding to his wife.

The interview with Bob's wife, Margaret follows:

1 **What message do you think Bob is trying to deliver by pushing around the linen carts?**

Bob worked for twenty-seven years at the airport as the night watchman. Part of his job was to walk throughout the airport monitoring the security. Bob always likes to be busy. He may be trying to let the nurses know that he wants to help them.

2   Yes, but sometimes when Bob pushes the other residents around, this may frighten them. Do you have some suggestions for how the caregivers can focus on Bob's remaining skills?

Nothing with Bob lasts for long. However, he does like to keep busy. Perhaps Bob could be allowed to push an empty linen cart around the unit. Or he could help to move the tables and chairs in the dining room to help the cleaning staff. Or he even could assist wiping the tables following meal times.

I am so sorry that he is upsetting some of the residents.

3   Talk about some ways that you are involved in Bob's care. And do you wish to be more involved in planning his care?

I took care of Bob for several years prior to his admission to Memory Care Manor. I trust that the girls are doing a great job caring for Bob. I do appreciate very much being invited to the conference when Bob's care is being discussed. I like to be involved in decision-making around Bob's care. For example, if his medications are being adjusted, I would very much appreciate being notified. Not that I could, or would change the outcome, but this helps me to understand Bob's behavior. The girls are really good about telling me if Bob needs anything, or how his day has been.

4   How do you handle it when Bob's things go missing?

This is an everyday thing with Bob. One week he lost his eyeglasses, dentures, one slipper, and hearing aide. These items all have Bob's name on it. Bob lives in the moment now and he needs very little "stuff."

I know that Bob goes wandering into others' rooms, and also that other residents come wandering into his room. I no longer get upset about things going missing. Bob's comfort and happiness is far more important to me.

5   **It is evident that you care for your husband. What information do the caregivers need to better understand Bob's needs?**

Bob has always loved dogs. We have a Collie dog named Sammy. If ever the girls are having a hard time with Bob, they only need to bring Bob his photo of Sammy; it's sitting right beside his bed. Seeing the photo of the dog might help "bring Bob back" when he is found wandering.

The other thing that works really well is to talk to Bob about his work at the airport. Bob loves to talk about airplanes and flying. This always brings him happiness.

6   **What things bring you happiness?**

That's a tough one. Bob and I have been together for over 50 years. This Alzheimer's disease has taken away the Bob I once knew. I want to hold him to the same standard of who he was before the illness.

Having said that, now that I understand this is an unrealistic expectation, I can accept and love Bob just the way he is. And being with Bob is all I want right now. I love him and I always will.

7   **What works best for Bob when he becomes restless?**

Bob likes to be busy and he loves to walk. Especially in the morning and again at early evening, Bob loves to walk. When I was caring for him at home and I could see he was becoming restless, I would just grab our jackets and say, "Okay, Bob, let's go take Sammy for a walk."

Analysis

Persons with dementia seem to enjoy wandering. To the outside observer, this wandering may seem to be serving no useful purpose. As in the previous chapter with Lydia, who may be preparing breakfast for her family in Russia, Bob also has his own reality. He may be looking for something, something he may no longer even be able to remember. At one level, Bob is searching for yesterday. When caregivers face this situation, they need to first assess, "Who is this person?" Professional caregivers may need to rely on the family to share biographical information about the person.

Although the individual may not be speaking, their body language is alive with feelings. Is the person happy or sad? Are they moving around in an agitated manner? Both family and professional caregivers will be empowered in Bob's care as they share information about who he is as a person.

Bob becomes easily agitated because he does not understand what is happening. Margaret is struggling because she no longer knows the person she has shared her life with. The professional caregivers may be struggling as well. They need to understand who Bob was before he became a resident at Memory Care Manor. In joining Bob's reality, caregivers appreciate that Bob is in the moment, and this moment for him is being the night watchman at the airport. He needs to be busy and may be trying to tell the nurses that he wants to help them.

A large part of caregiving is related to "the knowing," i.e. knowing who this person was prior to the development of dementia. Margaret knows that Bob likes to keep busy. She knows about Bob's personhood, and his sense of self. When caregivers have this information, they are then able to better embrace who Bob is, and to understand his emotions so much better.

This truly enhances the quality of life for Bob, empowering the caregiving success of both family and professional caregivers.

What Works:
- Understanding Bob's reality
- Joining Bob on his journey
- Keeping Bob busy

What Doesn't Work:
- Talking about Bob while he is present
- Preventing Bob from wandering
- Encouraging Bob to sit for long periods of time

4

Who is Fred?

washing the car

*A*lma and Fred have been married for 47 years; the last three years have been extremely difficult as Fred has been diagnosed with Alzheimer's dementia and Alma has been caring for her husband at home. Most recently Alma has noticed that Fred is becoming more and more forgetful and he increasingly displays poor judgment. Just the other day Alma saw Fred washing the car wearing his very best "Sunday suit." Today, following Fred's shower, Alma had laid out fresh underwear and clothing for him to change into. However, Fred was insistent that he wear the soiled shirt and trousers. When Alma tried to persuade him to put the fresh clothing on, Fred became loud and argumentative. Alma does not know what to do.

This dilemma is difficult for Alma on a daily basis. The immediate solution might be to allow Fred to wear the soiled clothes for now, and distract him into changing his clothes at a later time. Alma tried that and discovered that Fred is much

36

happier and more co-operative as a result. Family caregivers discover that letting go of their own reality, and joining their loved one on their journey, aids greatly in such frustrating situations.

The interview with Alma follows:

1   **How are things going?**

Pretty good; we take one day at a time. Fred is becoming more and more forgetful. This frustrates him a great deal, and I don't always know how to handle it.

2   **What happens when Fred becomes forgetful?**

We were at the shopping mall one day and bumped into an old friend who'd been a neighbor for many years and who we hadn't seen for some time. It was so good to see Charles and we had a really nice chat. When we said goodbye, Fred couldn't remember Charles' name. This upset him a great deal.

Fred will sometimes forget where he's placed his glasses or where the newspaper is. This bothers him. I try to change the subject; sometimes this helps.

3   **Talk about what you do when Fred gets upset.**

It is absolutely a waste of time to argue with Fred. Five minutes later he has totally forgotten what we were even talking about and then I'm the only one who is upset.

Instead, I try to change the subject and move on. That day, with getting Fred to change his clothes, I decided to lay out fresh clothing the night before and quickly hide the soiled things. Fred puts on the first thing he sees in the morning.

4   **What concerns you the most about this situation?**

Now that I reflect upon the situation, I guess I am expecting Fred to be the same person I have lived with all these years. Fred will always be Fred, but his behavior is so different now. The Alzheimer's disease has changed how he reacts to things.

5   **How do you deal with his poor judgment?**

I have discovered that if Fred's behavior is not hurting him or anyone else, then the best thing to do is to let the behavior go. In other words, I go with the flow.

These days, my favorite line is, "Forget about it."

So when Fred washes the car in his very best Sunday suit, I just make sure that there is a fresh suit and shirt in the closet for the occasion.

6   **When do you pause in the busy day?**

I pause a lot throughout the day. Fred and I start each morning with a 30 minute walk. I find this really helps to calm both of us for the day. I love to garden, and I love to read. Fred helps me in the garden and it offers both of us a nice pause in the day. It is so important to have many different things to break up the day.

7   **How does Fred help in the garden?**

Fred has always loved gardening. He loves to prune, he loves to plant and water the flowers. But I also feel he likes us to be together. He will wander around the garden, calling, "Yoo hoo, are you there Alma? Where are you Alma?"

I find he is much calmer following our time together outside.

8 **Explain how Alzheimer's disease has changed your family relationships.**

That's a tough question. Fred and I have been together nearly 50 years and yet, some days, I feel I don't know him at all. One day he said to me,

"Alma, how many kids do we have?"

That was pretty frightening for me. However, when I talked with other family caregivers at the Alzheimer's support group, some of them were going through the same phase, so I became assured about how normal this sort of comment can be.

When our daughter and sons drop by for a visit, sometimes Fred remembers their names and sometimes he doesn't. The children are wonderful, accepting their Dad just the way he is. I think our youngest son is having the hardest time.

9 **How do you think you could improve the situation for your son?**

The Alzheimer's support groups are very helpful. I meet so many wonderful people who are going through the same stuff we are. I guess it helps me just to share these experiences.

Fred has always been very close with the children, especially our youngest son, Matthew. It hurts him so much that his Dad can't remember all the good times they've shared together. But also, I believe Matthew is angry about what the disease has done to his Dad.

10 **How do you deal with the anger?**

The children see how Alzheimer's disease has changed their Dad, and how it has changed our family. As a wife and mother, I feel passionately about keeping the family strongly connected. We have round table discussions about how everyone can get involved with Fred. This helps me out a lot, and it also helps the children to deal with their anger.

Matthew and Fred actually managed to get out for some golfing on Saturday, which was good for them both.

Analysis

In the above situation, Fred's family members have an attachment to their own reality of who Fred was before the diagnosis of the disease. Fred is striving to conceal that anything is wrong and continues "to wash the car" as he always has. Fred feels he is still in control. Relationships with his children become problematic, as Fred can no longer remember past family memories. Alma no longer knows the man she's been married to all these years. This is indeed a time of confusion and chaos.

In dealing with the confusion and chaos, communication plays a critical role. The person with dementia is suffering from short-term memory, and may become easily agitated because he or she does not understand why they cannot remember. The person is living in the moment and past events with family are often forgotten. Asking too many questions may only cause agitation. Family members can best understand the journey by joining their loved one in their present state of mind, and "going with the flow."

In the Turmoil phase, family members struggle with the fact that they no longer seem to know their loved one. Fred is not the same person Alma has lived with all these years. Alma can expect that Fred will exhibit challenging behaviors. She can expect that there will be communication difficulties when Fred no longer is able to express exactly what he wants to say. Fred now communicates with feelings.

Families need assistance and support in understanding the journey. They are working very hard to catch up to the reality of where their loved one is on the journey. Time is running differently for Fred, and one of the best things this family can do right now is to focus on his strengths.

What Works
- Do not argue with the person
- Find humor in the situation
- Focus on strengths
- Purchase several similar outfits

What Doesn't Work
- Caregiver operating from within their own reality
- Logical reasoning
- Setting high expectations for person with dementia
- Arguing

5

Wish You Were Here

*this wife navigates early-stage Alzheimer's disease
with her husband*

I am sitting in the restaurant having lunch with my husband, Howard. But Howard's not here.

We ordered our lunch: minestrone soup (Howard's favorite), caesar salad, a nice panini bread, and tea. Howard excused himself, by saying, "I have to go to the bathroom, dear."

"All right," I responded. The soup came. I didn't want to start without Howard, but I was hungry. I finished my soup; still no sign of my husband. The salads arrived; still no Howard. The food items have taken on secondary importance.

By now, I'm beginning to wonder. I asked our waiter to please check on my husband. "He's been in the men's room for a very long time," I said.

The young man complied. Reporting back to me, he said, "Your husband says to tell you that he has to wait for his friend. In fact, the two of them are engaged in conversation."

"I don't understand," I said. "Howard went to the bathroom alone."

By now, the young man could see that I was becoming anxious. With a sigh, he said, "Okay, Madam, I'll check on him once again if you like."

And he did so. When he reported back to me, it was the most confusing and frightening message I have ever received.

"Your husband is talking to his friend in the mirror. He told me to tell you he can't join you for lunch until his friend is ready."

Peggy and Howard met nearly 45 years ago at a university dance. Peggy was studying nursing, and Howard, civil engineering. Peggy said, "I knew I was going to marry that guy when he offered to take me home from the dance with a bus ticket he found on the dance floor." They married three years later. Two children followed; a son and a daughter.

"Wish You Were Here" is based on a true story. Howard is in early-stage Alzheimer's disease. From the moment of diagnosis, his wife, family members and friends were thrown into a state of turmoil, struggling to understand and attach meaning to what is happening to Howard who has changed from the person they once knew.

The interview with Peggy, the wife follows:

1   Talk about how it was for you when Howard was diagnosed with Alzheimer's disease.

My first reaction was fear, but then, as strange as this may sound, the diagnosis almost came as a relief. I now can understand what has been causing Howard's strange behavior. And now I can also empathize with some of his fears.

2 **Can you offer suggestions for other families who are passing through a similar journey?**

The unsettling part of Alzheimer's disease is I don't know from one day to the next how Howard is going to react to different things. He said to me one day, "Peg, I can't remember from one minute to the next what I've done and what I haven't done."

What has really been most helpful is to draw closer with family and friends. We always have been a close-knit family and now I feel the children are even closer. I feel blessed to have them actively in my life. The best thing for us has been to take one day at a time. Some days, Howard seems like his old self again, and this gives me hope.

3 **Do you communicate with Howard any differently since the diagnosis of Alzheimer's disease?**

After more than 40 years of marriage, Howard and I are sensitive to one another's needs. I know his moods so it's easy for me to know when Howard is happy, sad, glad, or angry. I don't talk to Howard any differently, but I find he now communicates with feelings, not words. I noticed his mood change in the restaurant that day. Howard seemed to be getting agitated as soon as we arrived and needed to excuse himself.

4 **Are there times you have difficulty understanding what Howard is saying?**

I need to be sensitive to his body language and anticipate his needs. One day Howard wanted a glass of water and couldn't articulate the word "glass." This frustrated him a great deal. We played guessing games for a bit until I figured it out. Even that day in the restaurant, he was trying to tell me he didn't want to be there.

5 **How do you make the transition from being Howard's wife to being his caregiver?**

It's difficult. I had to realize that this disease is not about me. And yet some days I feel, "Hey, my needs aren't being met." Howard and I have always been very close, and we still are. Alzheimer's disease has changed our lives, but Howard is still Howard and I love him, whatever my role is. I will always be here for him.

6 **What made you choose that particular restaurant to have lunch?**

I have been told that a person with Alzheimer's disease needs an environment that is non-threatening, familiar, and simplified. Howard and I had been to that restaurant many times. On that particular visit, he no longer recognized the place or the waiter. I guess that means we are onto the next stage.

7 **Do you find that social situations have become awkward?**

Howard and I never have been social butterflies. We have a small circle of friends. However, I do find that we stay at home more now. That day at the restaurant was awkward; probably because the "mirror dilemma" was so shocking for me. I had a difficult time encouraging Howard to get to the car afterward. He didn't even eat his lunch.

8 **How did you eventually get Howard to the car?**

Good question. As hard as I try not to be embarrassed or humiliated by these things that happen in public, I am. I know that Howard doesn't function well with noise or distractions. I really should have been more sensitive to his body language at that moment. The waiter was terrific and so helpful in encouraging Howard to "excuse himself from his friend" and return to the table.

On the car ride home, we found humor in the situation. I find that it works really well to change the subject.

9   **Talk about some things in your home environment that you have changed.**

Howard's life is down to the basics. I've simplified the environment as much as possible which eliminates a lot of confusion for him. The fact that Howard was engaged in conversation with "a friend in the mirror" is an indicator that at times he no longer recognizes himself or others around him. It's interesting that Howard isn't bothered by the mirrors in our home.

10 **When do you pause in your busy day to take care of yourself?**

I give Howard a certain amount of my time as well as taking good care of myself. I maintain a healthy diet for both of us and we take walks together. I love that Howard still likes to hold hands as we walk along.

Howard loves to garden; he finds great joy in pruning the shrubs. I join him outside, both of us enjoying the fresh air and nature.

11 **Talk about how Alzheimer's disease has changed your family relationship and interactions with your children and grandchildren.**

The children focus on Howard as their Dad and their Grandpa, and not on the tragedy of Alzheimer's disease. Some days Howard doesn't remember our children's names. At one level, this hurts, but then I remember not to take it personally. We keep our love strong and our family strong.

I do try to keep family gatherings smaller now; Howard enjoys this closer interaction much more than being in large groups.

12 **What lessons have you learned from caring for your husband with Alzheimer's?**

Alzheimer's has robbed Howard of our ability to share memories. However, a person can still be someone without memories. We can still have a daily ongoing life without shared memories.

As things progress, Howard increasingly lacks judgment. The other day, he had his best suit jacket on to go out and wash the car. Now I can shrug about it—if the behavior isn't hurting him or others, then I let it go.

Howard gets upset with me when I try to do too much for him. So, I focus on what he still does really well. Howard makes an amazing pasta sauce and when we work together in the kitchen, I make sure that I'm the one to chop the veggies, for safety's sake.

Howard lives in the moment and I know he is "still in there." To me he is still a beautiful human being and the man I will always love.

Analysis

This is a time of chaos and confusion for this family. This is a time for understanding the needs of the person with dementia, and also for understanding the needs of the family caregiver. Peggy's family is attempting to understand and attach meaning to what is happening to a husband, father and grandfather who has changed from the person they once knew.

One of the greatest challenges in caring for people with dementia is that family and friends often try to maintain unrealistic expectations. They try to continuing holding their loved one to the standard of who they were before the onset of the disease. This can be extremely frustrating for both the person with dementia and their family and friends. Persons like Howard eventually only live in the moment. Family and friends are constantly playing catch-up to the person's deteriorating state of mind (see 4–T Dementia Care Model®, Page 12). As quickly as they may adjust to a new dimension or loss of function, there is another change. In this case, as Peggy realized during this visit to the restaurant, Howard no longer recognized the place or the waiter. This indicates a move onto the next phase.

As Peggy copes with her husband's early-stage Alzheimer's disease, she may be wondering, "Will we ever be normal again?" Family and friends caring for Howard do not understand right away what is happening. Although Howard is lacking in judgment, Peggy realizes that there are many things that he still does well and this is what she focuses on. They enjoy gardening together. Peggy loves that Howard still likes to hold hands on their walks together. And they work together in the kitchen, with Howard making his pasta sauce and Peggy chopping the veggies.

Alzheimer's disease has robbed Howard of his memories but Peggy is discovering that they can have a "new" life without their memories. Howard is living in the moment and his wife knows in her heart that her husband "is still in there." And that he's still a beautiful human being. As Peggy says, "Howard is still Howard, and I will always love him."

What Works
- Communicate with feelings
- Find humor in the situation
- Focus on strengths
- Simplify the environment

What Doesn't Work
- Environments that are unfamiliar
- Logical reasoning
- Overcompensating for what the person cannot do

Suggested Readings

Cohen, Donna & Eisdorfer, Carl (2001). *The Loss of Self: A Family Resource for the Care of Alzheimer's Disease and Related Disorders.* Norton.

Coste, Joanne Koenig (2003). *Learning to Speak Alzheimer's: A Groundbreaking Approach for Everyone Dealing with the Disease.* Houghton Mifflin.

DeBaggio, Thomas (2003). *Losing My Mind: An Intimate Look at Life with Alzheimer's.* The Free Press.

Shenk, David (2001). *The Forgetting: Alzheimer's: Portrait of an Epidemic.* Doubleday.

Phase 2

Transformation

butterflies are free

*T*he person with dementia is experiencing changes in behavior, nature and function. Just like a butterfly, morphing from its cocoon to setting itself free with wings, the person with dementia is transforming from one state of function to another. What is particularly interesting about this phase of the journey is that not only is the person's relationship to the world transforming, but their caregivers' thinking is also transforming about who this person was before. It often takes the family some time to catch up in their understanding as to where their loved one is today. However, when they do arrive at a new understanding, there is a sense of liberation from fears and worries.

Dementia has a way of softening a person's evident personality. There is no longer a strong expression of ego, leading the person to give up attachments to material things and social situations. The person is down to basics; licking a chocolate ice

55

cream cone makes them happy. Feeling the warmth of sunshine on their back makes them happy. The person with dementia has been transformed from one sort of functioning adult to another.

The thinking of family caregivers also needs to change as their loved one with dementia becomes, in a sense, a different person. A sense of liberation comes for caregivers as they acknowledge that this individual is changing. A husband reports, "I still hold my wife, Rose, to the same expectations I had before the diagnosis. This is extraordinarily frustrating for both of us. I know it's unrealistic, but I can't help it."

This phase, Transformation, will assist family and professional caregivers in understanding the journey. First, the true story will be revealed of the shared lived experience followed by the interview with the caregiver. We will identify some creative coping strategies, and conclude with an analysis of the situation. All of this empowers both the caregiver and the person with dementia. Caregivers will discover what works (and what does not) for each unique situation.

6

Hat Day at Daisy Park Manor

a Tweed English cap beckons a persistence of memory

*T*he following story depicts a situation at Daisy Park Manor where both the person with dementia and their caregivers are enjoying the moment.

The residents are gathered in a large circle of caring at Daisy Park Manor where they live. Many of them are suffering from a wide variety of problems that prevent them from keeping their own home any longer. And many have lost their physical independence as well. Mabel has a heart condition, Nicholas and John have Alzheimer's disease. Jimmy has had a stroke and can no longer speak. Then there's Florence, who suffers from dementia, and Phyllis who has arthritis and is confined to a wheelchair. Walter and Margaret have dementia and have both had a stroke. Lucy has Parkinson's disease. Ruth has diabetes. Bob has a heart condition. Vera is 100 years old and is bearing her age well, now confined to a wheelchair. Mary has arthritis and osteoporosis.

57

It is important to understand the diagnosis of each of these individuals in order to provide quality care for them. However, it is even more important to appreciate that there is a person beneath this diagnosis, someone with feelings, and one who can—if prompted—share a life full of rich experiences.

"Hat Day" is one strategy that is used to bring out the expression of deeper feelings and memories. It's a funny thing about donning a hat; there can be an amazing transformation of time and place. In the strategy called "Hat Day" the individual is drawn to a new landscape. This allows sometimes buried aspects of their personality to emerge.

Here's how it goes: each caregiver puts on a hat and then gives each of the residents in the circle their choice of hat as well. Most of the hats have a name and place on them. For example, some of the choices include baseball caps from teams in places such as New York City, Atlanta, Edmonton, Michigan, San Francisco; there are beach hats, a zookeeper's hat from the San Diego Zoo, football hats, soccer hats, and bicycle caps.

What seems like a magical transformation occurs when a resident puts on a hat. John is wearing a Laker's basketball cap. Previously, he'd been agitated and calling out for his wife. "Rose, Rose, where are you?" We now see John engaged with his caregiver about the days when he was a basketball player. John smiles as he tells about the many baskets he scored.

Jimmy's hat reminds him of the days he was a truck driver and he shares with everyone and anyone, that those "were the best days of my life."

Phyllis is wearing a beach hat that reminds her of all the fun she had playing with her sister Margaret at the beach. Mabel's hat is a baseball cap; this brings out wonderful memories of watching her grandson playing baseball.

Nicholas has donned a tweed English cap, which leads him to reminiscing about playing his harmonica, as he did in childhood. The group is singing along as Nicholas plays the mouth organ.

"What do you want me to play?" says Nick. "I will play whatever you want."

Everyone joins right in, with tunes and hand actions for simple little tunes like:

"If you're happy and you know it,"

"You are my sunshine," and

"My darling Clementine."

Problems are momentarily forgotten at Daisy Park Manor during this time of transformation when residents allow themselves to be swept away to a different place and time.

And Nicholas has a smile of satisfaction on his face. He views the group to see that his mouth organ music has brightened the day for everyone.

An interview with one of the caregivers in this group follows:

1 **How are things going?**

Pretty good, this activity gives us extra time to spend with the residents, and to find out more about them.

2 **What does the "Hat Day" strategy do for the residents?**

It sweeps the residents away to a different time and place. There is an amazing transformation. Normally, we focus so much on the daily tasks: the washing and dressing and feeding. We need to spend more quality time engaging with the resident and this activity is an excellent way to accomplish that goal.

3 **How do you think this activity could be improved?**

Good question; it's already pretty good. I guess it would

be even better if we got the families involved as well. They provide us with information about the resident, which helps us to learn about their likes and dislikes.

4　**Talk about what transformations we may see in residents as a result of this session.**

Sure, there are so many. Let me see. John, for example, had previously been agitated, calling out for his wife, Rose, who died some time ago. The Lakers cap brought John right back to the moment when he was shooting baskets on the court.

Phyllis is always missing her sister Margaret. At this moment Phyllis is frolicking with her sister on the beach. As a result, Phyllis is more cooperative with her care. Nicholas has been playing the harmonica since he was a little boy, so he was all smiles as he connected with a positive aspect of his past.

5　**What lessons have you learned from "Hat Day?"**

I'm learning to appreciate more about who the person is behind their illness. Activities like "Hat Day" allow the residents to share many of their stories and from this we caregivers pick up a lot of new information.

6　**What other ideas do you have for encouraging the residents to share some of their stories?**

It's important to just spend time with them, and to listen intently. Also, finding out from families some of the person's social history is helpful for caregivers too.

7　**What support is needed to accomplish this?**

It takes time—we can always use more time for these interactive activities. All of us are generally so busy and so focused on getting our essential work done on time, we tend to forget to take the time to just sit with and listen to our residents. Taking time to listen is important for knowing who they are.

Analysis

This moment is all we have. For many of these residents at Daisy Park Manor, they no longer remember a lot of their past in any sort of organized fashion. They often do not have a happy future to look forward to (though in many cases they seem to become unaware of that fact). People with dementia become really good at simply enjoying the moment. In our story above, for residents like Nicholas, being in the moment means donning a tweed English cap and playing his harmonica. That simple role-play takes Nicholas back to a happy time when he was surrounded by family and friends.

Of course, first it is important to understand the medical diagnosis of people with dementia in order to provide quality hands-on care for them. However, it is equally important to appreciate that there is a person beneath this diagnosis, one who has feelings, and one who can still have a life full of rich experiences.

Many caregivers, both family and professional, spend a great deal of their busy day focusing on the disease and not the person. Techniques like "Hat Day" are tools to facilitate the sharing of rich life experiences, which is a critical component adding to the quality of care.

The different hats serve to transform the people who put them on, enabling the person to bring out old memories and allowing others in the room to find out new things about each other: Jimmy is driving his truck; Mabel is enjoying her grandson's baseball game.

Yes indeed, these individuals have many rich life experiences to share. Any techniques that allow the caregivers to understand and appreciate who each person really is are of course quite helpful.

What works:
- Take time to listen
- Lift the disease and focus on the person
- Share the family-lived experience

What Doesn't work:
- Focusing on the disease and not the person
- Reality orientation (John's reality is that Rose is still alive)
- Being task oriented

7

Flower Child

pansies discover the child within

*I*t is the month of May. June was born in the month of June. June's reality is that it is now June. This morning she is feeling out of sorts, thinking about all her losses. June has lost her spouse, her home, and recently her vision. And now she is beginning to lose her mind. Because of her blindness and being in need of constant care, June lives at Daisy Manor. She is not happy today and thinks she might just want to stay in bed. As June dwells on her not so happy thoughts, her caregiver, Jenny, comes in the room with a big cheery Good Morning.

"What are you so happy about?" snaps June.

"It's a wonderful morning June; it's spring time and the sun is shining," Jenny replies.

"I'm just thinking about my birthday in June and remembering the fun we used to have as children. Now I can't see anymore and all my family and friends are gone. I just want to be left alone."

Jenny is not discouraged by this response. She knows a little about June including that this woman has always enjoyed her garden.

"We'll be doing some flower arrangements this morning and I need your help! I know that you have a "green thumb" June. Will you come and help us?" says Jenny.

"There's nothing else to do here," says June. "So I may as well come with you. I don't know how I can help though without being able to see."

"I'm certain you can offer so much to the group, June. I am so happy you will join us!"

When they arrive at the flower session, there is a circle of friends sitting around the table—Victoria, Nancy, Barbara, Jason, and Mary. These residents live at Daisy Manor, and are busy making flower arrangements, visiting and sharing stories.

"Good morning, June," everyone chimes, as June joins the group.

"Good morning," replies June, as she smells the flowers.

"What is your favourite flower June?" Mary asks.

"I have always loved pansies," says June. "Because my Grammy always planted pansies."

Jenny helps June place a flower in the vase. "This petal feels so soft, just like silk," says June, her fingers caressing a few of the petals. "Is this a pansy? I used to have so many beautiful pansies in my garden. And when I was a small child, Grammy would say, 'Look Junie, they have a happy face; they are smiling at you.' I always think about my Grammy when we talk about pansies."

While Jenny helps June place the pansies in the vases, they continue reminiscing about June's gardening days. This draws June away from dwelling upon thoughts of her many losses. She has a smile on her face and a twinkle in her eye as she recalls the child within.

The interview with Jenny, the caregiver follows:

1 **How are things going?**

June enjoyed the flower session so much. Even though she is blind, she could still see the shapes of the petals in her mind's eye and feel their fullness with her hands. The floral scents must have been pleasant for her too.

2 **How long have you been caring for June?**

June has been living at Daisy Manor for over six years. I knew her husband, Ivan, and when he was alive he visited his wife every day, sometimes twice a day. June has not been the same since Ivan passed on. She seems to have lost her spark.

3 **What changes have you noticed during this time?**

June has been an independent spirit all her life. Now, due to all her losses including the blindness, the mental confusion, and losing Ivan and her home, she has lost the feeling of independence. She becomes depressed easily.

4 **How do the staff manage when June becomes depressed?**

Just like today with the flower session, we do our best to distract June. I find it best to change the subject, or go for a walk outside with her. The other important thing is to focus on her strengths, especially on the things that June still does well.

5 **What impact do activities, such as the flower arranging, have on June's care?**

She is much happier and more cooperative. I find that by stimulating other senses, like smell and touch, that we're not focusing on her blindness and the dementia.

6   **How is this working? How would you summarize it so far?**
    June gets really annoyed when we ask her questions that she can no longer answer, such as, "How long have you lived at Daisy Manor?" However, incorporating an easy activity like flower arranging into her daily life allows June to bring back her own memories of her gardening days, the scents and touch of the flowers, and exploring pansies with her grandmother. These memories bring her some joy, and we see a smile on June's pretty face.

Analysis

The flower session is transformative for June. June's reality is that she is suffering many losses and that some days are emotionally difficult for her. Her caregiver can help by remaining sensitive to body language. In other words, if the caregiver can determine that June is feeling out of sorts on a given morning, a much better plan for the caregiver is to be not quite so cheerful. Starting out with a calm, quiet approach, to first check out June's mood, is a successful option.

One of the greatest challenges in caring for persons with dementia is that both professional and family caregivers may maintain unrealistic expectations of behavior and interaction. Family caregivers may hold the one they love to the standard of who they were before the onset of the dementia.

People with dementia, like June, are living in the moment. At some moments June may feel she is losing her mind. As her caregiver, Jenny knows a little about June and knows that she enjoys gardening. This information is helpful for focusing on and bringing forward some past memories that have been pleasurable for June, so that she can be distracted from nagging negative thoughts. When June joins her circle of friends at Daisy Manor, she feels a sense of belonging when asked, "What is your favorite flower June?" It is important to have friends on the journey down dementia lane.

It can be very liberating for family caregivers in particular to transform their thinking about who the person was before the dementia diagnosis. Although June may no longer have vision or a clear thinking mind, there are many things that she still can do well (similarly with Howard in Chapter 5). June does a good job with flower arranging; she can still smell flowers and feel their textures.

What Works
- Be sensitive to June's body language
- Focus on strengths
- Utilize biographical information
- Stimulate other senses (smell, touch) ✓

What Doesn't Work
- Allowing person to isolate
- Focusing on deficits or losses
- Lengthy activity (20–45 minutes maximum)
- Asking too many questions

8

Parachute Game

this parachute transforms

*T*he residents of Lavender Lane are gathered in a Fitness Circle in the lounge. The recreation facilitator, Heather, is planning some fun and games for them with a huge parachute spread out on the floor in the center of the circle. Some of the members of the circle include Phyllis, Margaret, George, Elsie, Bert, Violet, Jimmy, Ada, Florence and Norman.

These residents do not talk much, in fact, they spend most of their Lavender Lane days sitting quietly in their rooms, watching the world go by. Nothing much exciting happens, except for today.

Heather explains to everyone about how the parachute operates; she then connects the hand of each resident to a handle attached to the parachute. On the top of the parachute sits a big blue balloon. She then turns on the "Swing" music. Bert's eyes light up at the sound of the music.

Heather then asks everyone to lean way forward. As they lean forward in unison, the parachute goes down and the balloon goes down; then she asks everyone to lean way back, the parachute mushrooms open to reach the ceiling and the big blue balloon goes up as well. When the residents realize what is happening, they smile with delight and carry on in unison, first leaning way forward, and then leaning way back. Elsie squeals in delight each time the parachute opens to reach the ceiling. Heather then changes the rhythm to move the group to a side-to-side motion, once again moving the parachute and balloon along with it.

From the residents' body language and their gleeful sounds, they are obviously pleased with the results. Phyllis' face becomes quite animated as the parachute opens and closes. When the circle of friends realize that they are actually making this happen with their own hands and arms, they feel empowered, excited, and energized for the remainder of the day. Smiles abound.

The interview with Heather, the recreation facilitator follows:

1   **How are things going with the recreation activities?**
    Wonderful, the residents love it. Group activities break the monotony of their day and bring the residents to a different place in their minds, if only for a short while.

2   **What is your desired outcome using the parachute game?**
    This is a marvelous activity. There are so many benefits. It is a social gathering but it also empowers the residents— their actions make things happen. A range of motion exercise is good for them. And it's just plain fun!

3   **How will you know you have achieved it?**

One only has to look around the room to see the bright smiles, animated faces, and hear the squeals of delight. Jimmy said, "That's the best time I've had since I was driving my truck!"

The staff report that following the activity the residents are less resistant to care, they communicate more, and their appetites improve.

4   **What kind of plan do you need to create this activity?**

It's important to have a diverse group of residents involved and to encourage each person to become involved in the activity. The staff help me to focus on the strengths of each person. For example, Phyllis has had a stroke and is weak on the right side. But she manages really well in this activity, by holding onto the parachute with her left hand.

5   **When planning this, how can you assess the strengths of each person involved?**

I usually have at least two assistant volunteers to help with the parachute game. In this way, each individual can participate as much as they are able.

6   **How would you describe this activity?**

Everyone leans way forward. As they do so in unison, the parachute goes down and the balloon goes down. Then everyone leans way back, the parachute mushrooms open to reach the ceiling and the big blue balloon goes up as well. This is good stretching movement for the residents. When they realize what is happening, they smile with delight and carry on in bending and stretching together.

7 **What support do you need for this activity?**

The volunteers help each resident hold on to a handle attached to the parachute. This keeps the parachute opening to reach the ceiling. I appreciate it when several staff can help to transport the residents to the activity.

8 **What is your perception of the current situation?**

Usually there's not a great deal of excitement here at Lavender Lane. This activity allows the individuals to feel excited and empowered. Residents are in a positive mood for the remainder of the day.

Analysis

Organized activities provide a variety of benefits for persons with dementia. They help enrich the person's life by alleviating the boredom of everyday routine. It is critical to provide some contrast to the regular daily tasks of getting up in the morning, getting dressed and eating breakfast.

Activities provide some normalization for residents, like George, who now lives at Lavender Lane.

The hat day activity (Chapter 6) created an amazing transformation of time and place for the residents at Daisy Park Manor. The individuals were drawn to a new landscape and their personalities changed as well. In much the same way, the parachute game creates a new landscape for the residents at Lavender Lane. This game allows each individual to do as much or as little as they can.

Physical exercise that results from activities will benefit the person with range of motion exercise and motivates further use of their muscles. Following the activity, the residents are somewhat energized, their appetites may improve, and often they are less resistant to care.

When caring for persons with dementia, it is important to inject humor whenever possible. The more we can laugh at ourselves and the situation, the better. Activities stimulate laughter, which in turn increase circulation, reduce blood pressure, relax muscles, promote brain functioning, and reduce pain by releasing endorphins into the bloodstream. Laughter is contagious. During the parachute game, Violet began laughing when she saw the parachute mushroom open to reach the ceiling. Soon, everyone in the circle of residents was laughing.

For persons with dementia, their life is made up of small, individual moments. It is important to remember this when planning an activity that the person may have difficulty learning or relearning. Residents are often not able to focus on games such as bingo. This activity would prove far too complex and overwhelming for someone with memory loss.

The parachute game is perfect for dementia residents, as it focuses on their strengths and what they can still do well. These activities tend to produce meaningful experiences, which contribute to enhanced self-esteem.

What Works?
- Memory is not essential to enjoyment
- Build activity around the resident
- Maximize the abilities of each person
- Break activities down into simple steps

What Doesn't Work?
- Rushing through an activity
- Noisy environment
- Activity that is too complicated

9

Little Billy

small child gets the job done

*B*illy is visiting his Great-Gramma Florence at Daisy Drive Manor today. Billy is two years old and does not understand the reason for the visit. Florence has Alzheimer's disease. She does not understand the reason for the visit either.

Down another corridor of Daisy Drive Manor, caregivers are struggling with Alfred. They are struggling to get Alfred to put his clothes on, to wash himself, even to have a sip of juice. Alfred lives at the care home because he has dementia. He does not see any need for all this fussing. Alfred has been labeled as being "a mean and nasty man" to the point that caregivers groan when assigned to care for Alfred.

Little Billy does not know about any of these things. He has just discovered a huge soft, bright ball that is cheerfully red, white and blue, and he is mainly interested in having fun with it. Billy only wants to bounce this ball with Florence and have fun. But, Florence has no clue as to what is going on, and she is not the least bit interested in this silly game. By now, Billy has forgotten the reason for visiting his Great-Gramma. He picks up the beach ball, which is almost as big as himself, and bravely toddles over to where "Mr. Mean and Nasty" is sitting.

The staff has totally given up hope in getting Alfred's care completed, or encouraging him to eat or drink. Billy giggles, gives the beach ball a little throw, and the ball lands right into Alfred's lap. This of course catches Alfred by complete surprise. He looks up to see a delightful smiling toddler standing there, holding up his pudgy little arms, waiting to catch the ball back. Alfred grins, and gently tosses the ball to Billy, who decides he might just hang onto the ball for a little while. He runs about with it giggling the whole time. When ready, he tosses it back to Alfred. This lovely game goes on for some time, attracting a crowd of spectators of other residents who live at Daisy Drive. They are cheering on, each time Alfred catches the ball, or Billy throws the ball. What fun!

A short time later when the game is done, one of the caregivers comes by with apple juice for everyone. Billy likes the juice and this time Alfred drinks his juice as well. This puts a smile on Alfred's face.

The interview with Alfred's caregiver follows:

1   **What seem to be the main obstacles in caring for Alfred?**

Just about everything seems to be an obstacle when caring for Alfred. He doesn't see any reason for bathing, dressing or eating. When we try to encourage him, he gets agitated with us and with other residents. I worry for their safety when he gets aggressive.

2   **What do you suggest when this happens?**

Alfred benefits from a quiet environment. It is best to leave him alone when he gets agitated, and then come back and try later.

3   **Are there some ways to give Alfred some sense of control in his care?**

Alfred likes to be in charge. He appreciates having some say in the decision-making about his care. The other day his son was helping to hang some pictures in his room, and asked, "Dad, where do you want these pictures hung?" The son reported that asking Alfred what he wanted, served to provide him with a sense of control.

4   **How do you think you could improve the situation?**

When Alfred gets really agitated, it is best to leave him alone, give him some time, and try again later. When I assist Alfred in care, I try to give him some easy choices. For example: "Which shirt would you like to wear today Alfred, the red one or the blue one?"

5   **What is your sense of the situation when the small child Billy was playing with Alfred?**

It was amazing. Alfred seemed to forget all about himself. The child caught Alfred by complete surprise so there were no expectations from either one of them. They were just having fun.

6   **What transformation did you witness in Alfred?**

Alfred was no longer bored. He was less resistant to care. His appetite improved and he started drinking fluids with only a bit of encouragement. And that afternoon, he had a nap. All that excitement with Billy made him tired.

7   How does this compare with the way Alfred was in the earlier part of the day?

That spontaneous ball-playing activity improved Alfred's mood. He really enjoyed the fun and companionship of the small child. He was much less resistant to care.

8   Would it be possible to have small children visit Daisy Drive Manor on a regular basis?

That's a really good point. I'm going to speak to the activities department about that. The other residents love seeing the small children as well. There were smiles everywhere that day when Billy was visiting.

9   What other ideas do you have that might work for Alfred and others like him?

We could do other meaningful activities and things during the day to alleviate the boredom, such as music therapy, planting in the garden, feeding the goldfish, and pet therapy.

10 What support do you need to accomplish this?

All of the staff are really busy caring for the residents. However, we could ask the assistance of family members and volunteers. In fact, I know one daughter who could bring her dog to Daisy Drive to visit the residents. They love pets.

11 When you stand back for a different view, what sense do you get about Alfred?

Alfred's world is shrinking. I think he is afraid; he knows he is losing control of his thoughts and feelings and this frightens him. It would be frightening for any of us.

Analysis

There is an interesting similarity between small children and persons with dementia. Neither one operates with much of an ego. This explains why we often see toddlers playing side by side in the sandbox, unaware of each other's presence. In this story Billy only wishes to play. He brings no expectations or ego to Alfred. On the other hand, Alfred finds enjoyment in this time with a small child. He is no longer feeling bossed around by the staff, as though he has been given an agenda, or bored by the inactivity at Daisy Drive Manor. Spontaneous activity with a young child alleviates this boredom.

Boredom is what we feel when our lives lack variety and spontaneity. In a nursing home, such as Daisy Drive, it is critical to create an environment where unexpected and unpredictable happenings can take place but which add value to the day's routine. Meaningful activities are essential to human health.

There are several benefits to the caregivers and other residents as well, when small children visit the nursing home. Primarily, interaction with small children helps the person with dementia be happier. Secondly, the staff is happier by no longer having to struggle with challenging behavior. Finally, when elderly people see small children, it gives them a fresh boost of energy (by perhaps reminding them of times with their own children) and helps to alleviate boredom.

What Works
- Allowing time for activities outside of regular care
- Offering choices in care
- Providing a quiet environment
- Facilitating meaningful activity

What Doesn't Work
- Forcing residents into structured activities
- Social isolation of the residents
- Caregivers being task-driven

Suggested Readings

Bell, Virginia & Troxel, David (2002) *A Dignified Life: The Best Friends Approach to Alzheimer's Care.* Health Professions Press, Inc.

Brackey, Jolene (2000). *Creating Moments of Joy: for the Person with Alzheimer's or Dementia.* Purdue.

Castleman, Michael, et al. (2000). *There's Still a Person in There: The Complete Guide to Treating and Coping with Alzheimer's.* G.P. Putnam's Sons.

Vienne, Veronique (2002) *The Art of the Moment: Simple Ways to get the Most from Life.* Clarkson Potter

Phase 3

Transition

I want to go home now

*W*hat is home anyway? What does home mean? Home is a place where a person can feel safe and secure; it is a haven for rest and comfort. Home is familiar to us, "a place where we can close our eyes really tightly, and walk around and find everything." This place of "home" may no longer work for the person with dementia, as they become increasingly confused by their illness. The person with dementia loses the capacity to remember the significance or meaning of things in their home environment. For example, family photographs may now only represent strangers and memorabilia becomes clutter. Not remembering details and people provides a great deal of anxiety and discomfort both for the person with dementia and for their family.

At this point of Transition there is a passage from one state or place to another. At an earlier time, promises may have been made, such as: "Dad, we would never move you to a nursing home. We'll always care for you at home." For many families, this unexpected moment of transition can mean having to break a well-intentioned promise.

In this phase of Transition, there is a shift in thinking on two levels: family members realize that their relative with dementia needs more hands-on care, and also that things are going to work out as best as they can.

This section about Transition will assist family and professional caregivers in understanding the journey. A true story will be revealed of a shared lived experience, followed by an interview with the caregiver to identify creative coping strategies. Then an analysis of the situation will be presented which is intended to empower both the caregiver and the person with dementia. Caregivers will discover what works (and what does not) for each unique situation.

10

Apple Pie Story

a daughter is a child who grows up to be a friend

*I*n this story, the daughter becomes her Mother's best friend as they navigate Alzheimer's disease together.

Rachel's mother, Shirley, is 82 years old and lives in Indiana, far from Rachel who is in Los Angeles. Shirley remains vibrant and highly independent but has episodes of short term memory loss and confusion.

One rainy Sunday, Rachel receives a phone call from Shirley. "Dear, I'm baking an apple pie this morning! How many apples shall I peel?"

Her mother has always been an expert baker, so Rachel wondered at this oddball question. "Well Mother, I think perhaps six apples should be about right." A few minutes later the phone rings again. "This is your mother calling, dear. I'm baking an apple pie, and I am wondering how long should it remain in the oven?"

Rachel assured her mother of the approximate baking time.

She was not all that surprised when the phone rang 45 minutes later. "Dear, this is your mother. Do you think the apple pie is ready to come out of the oven? It looks golden brown."

"Mother, it smells delicious." The aroma of cinnamon is wafting to me over the telephone.

"Good", says Shirley. "Out it comes from the oven, and I've set two plates out; I shall slice us each a piece dear."

"Lovely!" says the grown daughter, and they enjoyed this special moment of warm apple pie over the phone.

The above story evokes childhood memories many of us have shared with our own mother.

The interview with the daughter follows:

1   **Do you worry about your mother living so far away?**

I try not to attach worry. Mom has lived in Indiana all her life; her roots are there. Many of her friends still live close by. I'd love to have her living closer by us, but she simply will not leave her roots. And another thing—maintaining independence has always been very important for her. Assisting my Mom in maintaining her independence for as long as possible helps to outweigh my worry.

2   **What suggestions could you make for other families dealing with a similar situation?**

Keep in touch with ailing parents or relatives as best you can, and just know that your loved one is alive and doing the best they can. I chat with Mom just about every day. Sometimes she doesn't remember that I have called, but that's okay.

I think it's important to find out as much as you can about the local resources where your loved one lives (including neighbors who will help out). Once arrangements have been set up, then make a point of maintaining communication with whoever is providing these resources. It is also important to simplify the dementia person's environment as much as possible—it should be easy for them to find what they need.

3   **Tell me about some of the things you have in place for your mother to maintain her safety and independence.**

As mentioned earlier, my mother's independence is very important to her. She always has been an "in-charge kind of gal," and the thought of becoming dependent really frustrates her. So I try to focus on what she still does well.

We have Mom connected to a service called the Life Line—just as a safety measure in case of emergency. So, for instance, if my mother should fall or something like that, help is just a phone call away.

When other illness factors come into play, there may be more to consider. My mother has always been prone to bladder infections. Her doctor recommended that she drink more cranberry juice to help prevent these infections. The last time I visited my Mom, I assured she had a good supply of cranberry juice and reminded her to drink it at least twice a day. But as soon as I leave, she forgets about the juice. So, what I've done is to advise two of my mother's good friends of the situation. They live close by and bring cranberry juice to my Mom. It seems like a small thing, but it keeps her from becoming ill and reduces my worry.

4   **Your mother seems to be an expert cook. Were you surprised by the apple pie questions?**

Yes, at first, because my mother has always been a great cook. But since the diagnosis, I find that each day holds a new experience and a lessening of my Mom's memory skills. So, when the telephone rang and Mom had questions about the apple pie, I must say I wasn't really surprised.

5 **How has the onset of Alzheimer's disease changed your relationship with your mother?**

It may sound strange, but this diagnosis has actually brought us closer together. There is somewhat of a role reversal; it seems I have taken over the mothering role and that's alright with me. Mom has made so many sacrifices for me. Now it's my turn to support her. She will always be my mother and I love her dearly.

6 **Talk about some of your childhood memories.**

I have a younger brother, Peter. I remember I was about 7 years old and Peter was 5 years old. On Saturdays, Mom would always let Peter and I take over her kitchen and bake anything we wanted. If we ended up making a mess she didn't seem to mind. One Saturday, Peter and I decided to bake an angel food cake.

I was mixing the dry ingredients in the bowl; Mom was showing Peter how to separate the eggs so the whites could be beaten. For one moment, when Mom turned away to reach for something, Peter turned the mixer to the highest speed. Egg whites whipped up out of the bowl, hitting the ceiling. Peter and I both screamed. My mother looked up at the egg whites splattered all over the ceiling, and her only comment was, "Oh, I guess this is a good time to wash the kitchen ceiling."

7 **Does your mother remember this?**

Yes, she does. This amazes me, because she can't remember that we just spoke on the telephone yesterday. It must come from a different level of memory.

8 **Sounds like your mother has a good sense of humor?**

Yes, Mom always maintained a good sense of humor. She thought that childhood should be about building memories and having fun. She could always make us laugh and she always had a way of making things fun. Like the time Dad brought home the "biggest fish." Daddy had it all cleaned and ready for pan-frying. Mother called us for dinner when this was all ready and prepared. There in the middle of Dad's dinner plate was this teeny, weeny sardine fish! We laughed so hard.

9 **Even with the Alzheimer's disease, does she still retain her sense of humor?**

Absolutely! Alzheimer's disease has robbed Mom of many of her memories, but not her heart. She no longer remembers a lot of the things we did together years ago but her sense of humor is alive and well. Some of Mom's brightness is vanishing but we are making new memories every day. We still laugh a lot.

Analysis

Maintaining a safe environment for the person with dementia, while not compromising the individual's independence and dignity, can be one of the greatest challenges of coping with this disease. Because of this, frustration levels can run high, both on the part of the person with dementia and their caregivers.

This daughter believes that her mother's independence and sense of control in her life outweighs the option of moving her mother close, presumably for greater safety. Helping her mother be as independent for as long as possible seems to outweigh the worry.

When families face this situation, they need to first assess what's going on with their loved one. Independence is very important for Shirley. She always has wanted control and to be in charge. Knowing this, the family has connected her to the Life Line as a safety measure. In case of emergency, or if she should fall, help is just a phone call away.

This daughter keeps in touch and chats with her mother just about every day. And she has found out as much as possible about the local resources where her Mom is living and remains connected with these resources. This continued contact is reassuring for the daughter.

Although home is a place of comfort, safety and security, and while Shirley's independence is very important to her, her daughter fears that her mother may no longer be safe in her home. Rather than making a transition at this time, the daughter has found out as much as possible about the local resources where her mother is living and remains connected with these resources. This daughter focuses on her mother's strengths.

And at this moment, she can still smell the cinnamon from her mother's apple pie.

What Works
- Focus on strengths
- Maintain independence for as long as possible
- Simplify environment
- Remain connected with local resources

What Doesn't work
- Unfamiliar environment
- Logical reasoning
- Bossing, telling parent what she can and cannot do

11

Kay

knowing the right time to move

Kay is being admitted to the Special Care Unit of Tick Tock Manor. This is a specially designed unit which is "locked and keyed" for persons with Alzheimer's disease and related dementias. Kay is accompanied by her daughter, Judy.

From the moment they step off the elevator, Kay begins shouting, "I'm not staying here, and you can't make me stay here." Judy attempts to calm her mother, with no effect.

This only provokes Kay more. "If you make me stay here, I will kill myself," says Kay as she takes off, pacing down the hall. She is carrying a handbag, swinging it as she goes, including at anyone who comes near or talks to her.

One of the caregivers says to Kay, "Would you like a glass of juice?" Kay screams back forcefully, "I TOLD YOU, I'M NOT STAYING HERE!"

Another caregiver offers to help Kay remove her coat, but this only agitates Kay further. She charges down the long hallway of Tick Tock Manor, hitting anyone she can reach with her handbag.

The above illustrates a situation where Kay's anger is out of control. In moment's like this, Kay feels misunderstood and abandoned and she refuses to be consoled. Her daughter does not know what to do.

The interview with the daughter, Judy, follows:

1   **Have you been taking care of Kay at home?**

Yes, since her diagnosis four years ago. Though it seems much longer. She has become more and more disoriented.

2   **Can you explain how you sensed that the time was right for Kay to move?**

In some ways I seemed ready for the move before my mother. I was exhausted most of the time with my whole day spent caring for her. In fact, I had no other life. Also, my Mom was surrounded by things in her home that she could no longer remember, and this was upsetting for her. Now in the care home, she asked me the other day, "Whose house is this?"

3   **How can the caregivers best assist Kay?**

My mother needs a calm, quiet approach. The important thing for caregivers is to allow Kay to have space, especially when she is agitated. They need to observe her body language, especially the expression in her eyes. Are Kay's eyes portraying that she is happy or sad? Do her eyes say "Welcome" or "Go away!"?

4　**Did you visit many homes before choosing Tick Tock Manor for Kay?**

At least 50. Some of them were horrid. People were tied into their chairs; some were over-medicated and sleeping all the time.

5　**How did you know that Tick Tock Manor was the right choice?**

I'm so glad you asked that. I knew as soon as I walked in the door. I could feel the positive, supportive energy. Actually, at Tick Tock Manor, they seem to allow the person with dementia to live out their dementia, each in their own way.

6　**What advice can you give to other family caregivers about moving their loved one?**

I would strongly advise them to not discuss the move ahead of time. And be proactive for them. Kay is so vulnerable right now and I am the only one to care for her. The other thing is to not treat your loved one's complaints lightly. In other words, when Kay gets upset, I pay attention. Always be there for them and offer support, no matter what.

Analysis

During this phase, a major move is about to happen. A move from one residence to another. This daughter may have made a promise to her mother—a promise to Kay that she would never move her to a nursing home. But the dementia progressed and the care load became too heavy. So this daughter has had to break a promise.

It is a difficult time in the journey for the family, determining the right time to move their loved one. The daughter is ready for this transition, but is her mother, Kay, ready?

As soon as Kay walks off the elevator of Tick Tock Manor, her anger bursts out of control. When introduced to a new environment, persons with dementia may suffer relocation trauma. This means they may require time to adjust to all the newness of the place. Even as Kay's daughter attempts to calm her, she becomes more agitated. Kay's reality is that she is being abandoned at Tick Tock Manor.

When family caregivers, like Judy, enter this phase of Transition, they change their thinking about who their loved one is today. Judy will feel liberated as she changes her thinking about her mother.

What Works
- Utilize distraction
- Simplify environment
- Allow time, have patience
- Obtain biographical information from family caregiver

What Doesn't Work
- Arguing with the person
- Environment that is over stimulating
- Rushing the person with dementia
- Entering the person's personal space
- Discussing the move ahead of time

12

Bessie

this caregiver has a transition in thinking

*B*essie is a long time resident at Memory Care Manor. She suffers from Alzheimer's disease. Also, several years ago, Bessie suffered a stroke and as a result she cannot tell the caregivers what she wants and does not want. She is confined to a wheelchair. She shares a table in the dining room with three other residents. Immediately adjacent to their table is a door, which provides a short-cut leading back to Bessie's room. She always takes this route following mealtimes.

However, today after lunch, when Bessie wheels herself through this door, there happens to be a meeting taking place there. This does not deter Bessie. Oh no. She proceeds to wheel herself through the room anyway, heedless of the power cords and chairs, which are obstructing her route. When the caregiver attempts to explain to Bessie that she cannot possibly come through here today and will have to re-route, this only causes Bessie to push her wheelchair even harder. A battle ensues, whereby the caregiver attempts to push Bessie's wheelchair in the other direction.

Finally, a catastrophic reaction results with Bessie screaming, "Let me go, let me go." This causes the caregiver to change her thinking, and she moves all the chairs and power cords out of the way. Bessie then wheels herself through the crowd to her room waiting on the other side.

The interview with Bessie's caregiver follows:

1   **How are things going?**

Actually, not so well. Bessie has been having several angry outbursts. She can't tell us what she wants and when we misunderstand she gets frustrated. She hit one of the ladies in the dining room the other day.

2   **What do you think Bessie may be trying to tell you?**

Perhaps that she still needs to be in charge and in control of her life. Bessie's son tells us that his Mom has always been very independent.

3   **What would be an example of that?**

Like when she wheeled herself through the meeting room. Bessie has decided that's the way she's going and no one is going to change her mind.

4   **What concerns you the most about this situation?**

Bessie's safety. The power cords and chairs were obstructing her way and it was not safe for Bessie. In reflection, it would be easier to simply remove the obstructions and allow Bessie to have her way.

5   **You believe Bessie may not be safe?**

It seems she becomes more confused each day and her judgment is negatively affected. I am afraid she may fall trying to make her way around all those chairs in the room.

6   **What is your desired outcome?**

The best possible quality of life for Bessie.

7   **If the same thing came up again, what would you do?**

Allow Bessie to have her own way. It is a waste of time and energy to argue with someone who wants their own way; she often can't remember what the argument was even about. The important thing is to assure her that her environment is safe.

8   **What impact does it have on Bessie to have some control over her own care?**

Bessie needs to have a sense of control over her environment. By allowing her to wheel herself through the meeting room, she is changing what she can. As a result, her levels of frustration and agitation are decreased, and the staff is pleasantly surprised that Bessie is more cooperative in care.

Analysis

As the above illustrates, Bessie may no longer have the ability to be logical or rational. The caregiver has one plan and Bessie has another. Persons with dementing illness discover that their world is shrinking. They may no longer recognize the environment in which they live. Bessie needs to be able to alter her environment and change what she can. A similar set of circumstances occurs in Wheelchair Ballet (Chapter 2), where Lydia has her own reality and is trying to find a different place. Bessie also becomes easily agitated as she attempts to navigate her way around Memory Care Manor.

It's important to give conscious thought to "creating contrast" for individuals such as Bessie and Lydia as they feel their world shrinking. How can we preserve their world as they once remembered? What is Bessie thinking as she is wheeling herself from dining room to bedroom, meal after meal, day after day?

Quality of life care is very important for Bessie but caregivers are striving to remove some of the monotony from her days. In some ways this is a paradox, because routine and structure are important for persons with dementia. Routines and structure ensure that important aspects of care are done. But at the same time, in planning the activities of daily living (such as dressing, grooming, hygiene, and mealtimes), caregivers need to be conscious of creating contrast. Bessie's caregiver might offer her choices in clothing, or she might offer to take Bessie for a walk in the garden and introduce her to the house cat, Felix. Always remembering, Bessie needs to feel safe and secure in her environment as well.

A husband reports, "Every day is the same. It doesn't matter if it's July 4 or Christmas day. My wife is stuck in her wheelchair and with her losing her mind as well. It doesn't matter what day it is." This husband's world is shrinking as well. He needs to feel empowered and to be able to change what he can. It is critical that professional caregivers understand this.

Caring for persons with dementia can be emotionally and physically draining for both family and professional caregivers. Perhaps the concept of creating contrast is equally important for the caregiver as well as the person they are caring for.

In other words, caregivers must give themselves permission to maintain a healthy lifestyle away from the duties of caregiving.

What Works
- Simplify environment
- Maintain structure, routine
- Create contrast
- Assure safety

What Doesn't Work
- Logical reasoning
- Arguing with person
- Forcing change on independent-minded people

13

Where is Harry?

this wife shares how she does not lose hope in caring for husband in late-stage Alzheimer's disease

*A*lzheimer's disease is a progressive, irreversible, and neurological disease with presently no cure. It affects not only the person afflicted, but by consequence also the entire family.

This medical information and the reality about a revised family situation is not particularly encouraging; in fact, knowledge of the realities offer little hope to family members. However, in sharing the lived experience with one such family member, Jean reports, "I took care of Harry at home for seven long years prior to admission to the nursing home. Now, I give Harry only so much of my time. I do manage to get up for a visit every day. I don't think it much matters though, because Harry doesn't recognize me anymore. One day, when I arrived, Harry was holding hands with one of the female residents."

One can appreciate the sense of loss and despair that Jean felt in that moment.

Jean went on to say, "I know that Harry is being well cared for here, but gosh I am lonely. In preparing for a move and sizing down, I have sold the house and given away all of Harry's things. I know there is little hope for curing Alzheimer's disease, but I sure do hope now that they don't find a cure—if Harry comes back, and finds that I have given away all of his things, he will kill me!"

The above dialogue illustrates a situation where the family member is hurting so badly from the loss of relationship with her husband, Harry, that she compensates with humor. It is critical for Jean to incorporate some self-care practices into her daily life in order to maintain her own health. In caring for self, Jean will be empowered to care for Harry.

Interview with wife, Jean follows:

1   **Talk about how you handle it when Harry no longer recognizes you.**

This part is really hard for me. It doesn't seem to matter if I visit or not. Whatever, I just take one day at a time. Harry's doctor tells me it is important to visit, so I do. I trust that it makes a difference.

Last month I was away visiting our son for three weeks. When I got back, I was nervous coming by to see Harry, not quite knowing what to expect. Anyways, when I came around the corner and Harry saw me, he said, "Where the H—— have you been?"

2   **When did you first begin to notice that something was wrong with Harry?**

There were so many little signs, it is hard to say. I remember, one day last year, Harry started to forget where rooms are. Or, he would go to the bathroom to use the toilet, come back, get up and say I have to go to the toilet. Some days, Harry goes back and forth to the bathroom over and over, without even using the toilet.

The other thing, is that Harry really likes his morning cup of coffee. This is the way he has always begun his day. Now, when I set the cup in front of Harry, I have to remind him to drink it, as he often forgets the cup is there.

3   **You are Harry's wife. How do you handle your duties as his caregiver?**

I give Harry only so much of my time. Even before Alzheimer's happened, Harry and I led very independent lives through our jobs. He went to his office each morning, and I went to mine. What's so different now is that I have to be the strong one. I have to be the one in charge and in control. The other day he looked me straight in the eye, and he said to me, "You won't ever leave me Jean, will you?"

4   **How do you deal with the silence?**

Most of the time Harry just grunts if he doesn't like something. At this stage, I find that Harry no longer communicates with words but with feelings. After all these years of being together, we are sensitive to each other's body language. I can tell whether he is happy, sad, angry, or glad.

5   **What strategies can you share with other family caregivers traveling a similar journey?**

One of the greatest difficulties in caring for Harry has been that I started out with unrealistic expectations. I wanted to hold Harry to the same standard of who he was before the Alzheimer's disease. Over time that was increasingly frustrating for both of us.

When I realized that Harry had changed and that he lives in the moment now, our lives changed in a positive way. Each day is a constant learning experience for both of us. I will always love Harry because he is so loveable.

6   **Did you ever feel you couldn't handle it any more?**

Some days I am so lonely. That is the hardest part for me. I do many things for myself. I get my hair done once a week. Every morning I go swimming before I come to visit Harry. And once a week I get together with a close friend for a chat. It helps to stay connected with family and friends.

7   **Do you find that family and friends visit less often?**

Not really. Our family has always been close. I know that the children have busy lives of their own and I try not to burden them. One of them will visit just about every day, seeing how we are doing. It sounds strange, but in some ways, I think this Alzheimer's disease has brought our family even closer together.

8   **Talk about ways you are preparing for the next phase.**

Harry has always been a very organized person. Over the years, he taught me to have things in place and ready ahead of time. So, when the diagnosis of Alzheimer's disease came, I said to the children that I want to have things in place, while I still have my wits about me.

Harry and I already had our Living Wills drawn up. However, I called our lawyer to go over the documents once again. Our son holds the Power of Attorney.

I couldn't possibly keep up the house and yard by myself, so I have down-sized and sold the house. I live in a smaller place closer by, so I can see Harry daily.

It hurt me a lot to give away Harry's things while he is still alive. But Harry lives in the moment now. He is down to basics. All he has in his pocket is his billfold and I think there is only one blank check in it.

Analysis

This wife gives Harry only so much of her time. He used to be the one in charge, now it's her role to run the show. Being the strong one now feels different for the wife; she has to be in charge and in control. At one level this means breaking a promise by moving her husband to the nursing home. This is very difficult for her because she can remember Harry saying to her, "You won't ever leave me Jean, will you?"

There is a transition in Jean's thinking as she realizes that Harry no longer recognizes her. As mentioned earlier, Jean had been trying to hold Harry to the same standard of who he had been before the Alzheimer's disease. She finds herself back in the phase of Turmoil, needing to understand "the new Harry," a person she knew as a much different man to the one she cares for today.

When she arrives for a visit and he is holding hands with another female, Jean makes a conscious decision that Harry's spirit is alive and well. Her thinking is transformed. This is a sobering but liberating moment for Jean, understanding that Harry lives in the moment now.

As Jean's thinking changes, she realizes that she only can give Harry so much of her time. She is grieving the loss of the Harry she once knew, while preparing for a move and down-sizing (she has sold the house of their marriage and lives in a smaller place close by so she can visit Harry every day). Also, she incorporates some self-care practices into her daily life in order to maintain her own health; caring for herself empowers her to care for Harry.

What Works
- Knowing the right time to move
- Investing time in self-care
- Focusing on the moment

What Doesn't Work
- Maintaining unrealistic expectations
- Neglecting self-care
- Family caregiver being isolated from family and friends

14

Phyllis

How is Mother doing?

*P*hyllis is 92 years old, suffers from dementia and resides at Memory Lane Manor. Over and over, Phyllis will ask
her caregiver, Frances, to take her home. She wishes to see her
Mother there who Phyllis says is waiting for her. Phyllis' entire
face lights up in anticipation to see her Mother.

Frances states, "You must miss your Mother very much."

Phyllis: "Oh yes I do, and I love my Mother."

Frances replies, "And I'm sure your Mother loves you very
much."

Phyllis: "Oh yes she does."

Frances says, "Tell me about your Mother, Phyllis. What
does she look like and what color is her hair? What color sweater is she wearing?"

Phyllis responds, "My Mother has brown hair; she is very
pretty. She is wearing a blue sweater."

Frances says, "I am sure she is very pretty, just like you are very pretty. Shall we go and have a cup of tea and talk some more about your Mother?"

Phyllis says, "Yes, I would like that."

As they are chatting over a cup of tea, Phyllis continues, "And I love my sister Margaret so much. She is 8 years old."

"Is Margaret warm enough?" asks Frances.

"Oh yes, Mother would make sure she wears her sweater. And my mother is going to church with her friends today. She is wearing her hat."

"It is Thursday today. Is this a special day?" Frances asks.

"I go to exercise classes today. I always like to learn new things," says Phyllis.

Phyllis' niece, Susan, just now enters the room.

"You've grown so much, I didn't know who you are," Phyllis says to her now grown-up niece who is visiting her at Memory Lane Manor.

"I'm so happy to see you Auntie," responds Susan.

"And Margaret tells me you are doing so well in school," states Phyllis.

This last remark particularly pleases Susan, as Margaret is Phyllis' sister and actually, Susan is a high school teacher. Susan is delighted that her aunt remembers.

"Yes she did, and yes she did," says Phyllis. By focusing on her remaining skills, Phyllis' quality of life is enhanced.

"What's that?" Phyllis asks her niece.

"It's your pink hat," says Susan.

"It looks like a pancake," responds Phyllis. "She likes to make jokes," Phyllis says as an aside to Frances.

"Do you want to wear it today?" asks Susan.

"Oh yes," says Phyllis. "I'm never going to forget this day."

"Mother will be wondering why I'm not home for supper," adds Phyllis. "Yes she will, and yes she will."

The interview with Susan, the niece, follows:

1   **How is it going?**

Actually, really well! Each visit with Auntie Phyllis is so different. I am so pleased that Auntie recognized me today. Most visits, she doesn't. And today, she enjoyed reminiscing about her sister, Margaret, who is my mother. I love listening to the stories she tells of growing up.

2   **How has your thinking changed about the situation with your Aunt Phyllis?**

I understand that Auntie Phyllis is in her own world now. She lives in the moment. This transition in my thinking has been liberating for me. Most days, when I visit Auntie, she is content, and that is what matters.

3   **How do you handle Phyllis being in her own world?**

Auntie cannot remember many things from the past. In fact, asking too many questions gives her a great deal of anxiety. So the best thing is to allow her to have her own reality. This is different from my reality, but this is not about me. I try to "go with the flow."

4   **How is your Aunt Phyllis different from the Phyllis you once knew as a child?**

I remember my Auntie Phyllis has always been a fiercely independent spirit. In spite of the dementia, I still see that piece of her personality shining through. Her eyes are twinkling. She tells the girls exactly what she likes and doesn't like.

5 **Give some examples of the old personality shining through.**

For sure. One day the staff were preparing to give Auntie her bath. She screamed at them, "If you don't remove yourselves from my room this instant, I am going to call the police."

6 **What happened then?**

At first, they didn't listen to her. Auntie Phyllis kept on screaming and hissing at them. Then one of the girls who knows Auntie entered her room to assist. She calmly approached Auntie, reminiscing with her about Mother and Margaret. This totally distracted Auntie away from the bathing idea, and the caregivers proceeded to get their job done.

7 **What has home meant to your Aunt Phyllis?**

Everything. Auntie has been a homemaker all her life. She loved cooking, cleaning and decorating. She and my Mother would bake endlessly. They were so good together in the kitchen. Home has always been a place of comfort for Aunt Phyllis.

8 **So what do you make of all that?**

Some days Auntie thinks Margaret is still a little girl and they are playing together at home. Some days she thinks Mother is right here taking care of them both, and bringing them home from school. I just try to go along with Phyllis wherever she is in her thoughts.

9   **What lessons have you learned from caring for your Aunt?**

I have learned the wonderful art of letting go of my own agenda. It's not always easy, however, the visits with Auntie are ever so much better and richer for it. Thinking I was her sister, one day Auntie said to me, "Come sit on my lap Margaret." So I did. She bounced me on her knee for a minute, smiling and giggling with delight. Later, I thought to myself, what does it matter if Auntie thinks I am Margaret? She is happy, and that's what counts.

Analysis

The above conversation with Phyllis clearly illustrates that she is remembering her past, and has some fond memories of her childhood. As Phyllis is searching for yesterday, her caregiver can join her in reminiscing, by asking questions pertaining to her loved ones. For example:

- What games did you and Margaret play together?
- Did you hold hands when you were walking to school with Margaret?
- What was the color of the hat your mother was wearing to church?

Today has proven to be a wonderful interaction, both for Phyllis and her niece. Focusing on Phyllis' remaining skills has empowered and enhanced her present quality of life.

It helps Phyllis to compensate for any lost abilities by not bringing them to her attention.

"Where is my sister?" asks Phyllis.

Persons with dementia of the Alzheimer's type may get lost in their memories. They may think they are in an entirely different place. Ideally, the caregiver should allow this moment; the individual may wish to discuss the past.

"It's really Margaret I'm worried about," says Phyllis. "Where is Margaret? Are you going to put Margaret on my lap? She will sit right here. That's the best and easiest of all."

In the above illustration, Phyllis is worried about her little sister, Margaret, who she remembers as being nine years old. It is breakfast time and her caregiver assures Phyllis that Margaret can sit on her lap for breakfast. In this way, Phyllis is allowed some choices, making partnering with her caregiver even better.

When Phyllis sees her niece, Susan, she once again returns to her childhood, with dear memories of her sister. It seems that persons with dementia must take a leap back into their youth as their dementia progresses.

In this phase of the journey, there is a transition in thinking, as Susan realizes, "Auntie Phyllis is trying to tell me something, and I think it's going to be alright."

What Works
- Calm approach
- Distraction
- Focusing on remaining skills

What Doesn't Work
- Logical reasoning
- Arguing with Phyllis
- Asking too many questions

15

Evelyn

discovering sameness in change

Evelyn is going through a transition. She did not ask for this change. First her husband died. Then her driver's license was revoked and her automobile was sold. Now she is losing her vision and being told she has to move from her home. Others are telling her what to do, bossing her around, and it's not fair. She has just moved into Wildflower Manor, an Assisted Living setting, and it is simply too much for Evelyn to handle all at once.

Even with the change of residence, Evelyn demands a certain amount of sameness in her life. The pictures must be hung in exactly the same spot above the sofa in the living room. The three hooks are lined up in the closet where they were before. The dishes are placed in the cupboard above the sink, the canned goods are on the bottom shelf, the cutlery drawer is to the right of the dishwasher, and the kettle sits on the back right stove burner, just as in her previous home. Evelyn's medications are lined up on the right side of the refrigerator. And beside the toaster is her coffee maker, already prepared for the morning.

When the furniture is dusted, she returns all of the precious china ornaments to the same positions on the embroidered cotton as they were in Evelyn's previous home. Family photographs sit on the table in their proper places. The photos of grandchildren's smiling faces light up the bedroom. Above the bed hang the memories of loved ones in photos outliving their memory. The clock chimes the time; these days, time for Evelyn marches on as if on crutches. This same clock hangs on the same wall for her, only this wall is in a new home.

As Evelyn awakens to the clock, she walks to her small kitchen (using her cane), turns on the light over the stove, and switches on her ready coffee maker. She then makes her way to the bathroom, a few short steps away, and plants her teeth back in her mouth. They have been sitting in the same "pink Grammy's denture cup" in the right corner of the bathroom counter. A few combs through the hair assure Evelyn that the strands are in place, and she completes her morning routine.

The morning medication routine is the same for Evelyn. She counts out her same nine pills, as she measures her mouthful of coffee and her pills. Evelyn then assures that her medication supply is in her purse that she will be bringing with her to church this morning. With a sigh, she sits down in her comfy chair, looking through her purse, and says, "Where are my keys dear?"

I know these things to be true, because you see, Evelyn is this author's mother.

The interview with daughter follows:

1 **How are things going?**

This is a very difficult time for my mother. It seems for her that all her losses have come about at the same time. Losing Daddy was hard enough. But then within six months her driver's license was revoked. This was a devastating blow to my mother's independence.

And then the car was sold, and now she is losing her vision, and being told she has to give up her home. Things are moving much too quickly for my Mom and she doesn't like it.

2 **How did you know it was time for the move?**

My brothers and I have been concerned for some time about the safety issues for Evelyn. It seems as though overnight her vision has deteriorated quite rapidly. She has difficulty managing kitchen tasks. Getting around is another big issue for my Mom; her arthritis is so painful. And lately, she has been isolating herself, and not getting out to visit with her friends.

3 **Was Evelyn ready for the move?**

Mom's home and family have been her whole life. Asking her to give up her home was a very difficult thing to do. It will take time for her to adjust.

4 **How does she feel about Wildflower Manor now?**

I asked Mom the other day, "Are you making new friends there?" She responded quite matter-of-factly, "You don't make new friends at my age Dear."

However, when I visit with her, she seems to be engaging with others. She is becoming involved with activities, and appears to be not so isolated. I called my Mom one cold, wintry day, when it was icy and snowing outside, and she reported, "I've had my hair done, had a wonderful massage, the podiatrist has done my toes, I went to bingo, and I haven't even left the building."

5   **What concerns you most about where Evelyn is now living?**

It would be the risk of falling, and the problems related to her impaired vision. So, now I visualize my mother as walking strong and tall, with her feet safely planted on the ground.

I asked the Wildflower Manor management to disconnect the stove burners, because I am afraid of the fire hazard. Mom got really angry with me, and had the stove reconnected.

6   **Describe some of the changes you have seen in your Mother since this move.**

In many ways, Evelyn is more in charge of her life at Wildflower Manor. She attends the council meetings and provides input about the dining experience, the activities, and the church services. She is making "new acquaintances" every day. I find that since Evelyn has moved here, she is far less self-centered. She is more outgoing and simply happier.

7   **What is your sense of how this is going to work out?**

That's a good question. It's best to take things one day at a time. I pray my mother won't fall. I pray for her safety every day. At this moment, my main concern is for her happiness and quality of life. Naturally, one can't be happy every minute. The other day when we chatted, Mom said,

"Your Father and I would have been married 60 years this year, if he were still living," and she started to cry.

8   **What supports do you need to have in place to assure success for your mother living at Wildflower Manor?**

It's critical to keep in touch with the management at Wildflower Manor. The staff working here are very good and available 24 hours a day. The one time last year when my mother got an infection, they were prompt about calling an ambulance.

Also, my mother has a very good friend who I keep in close contact with. That friend checks in regularly with my Mom and keeps me informed of any problems or concerns. And my brothers both live close by, so they also have opportunities to be supportive.

9   **Any other thoughts to share?**

It was a very tough decision for us all to move my mother to an assisted living setting. But knowing how important her safety needs are, and knowing what home means to her, my brothers and I strived to meet her needs for both comfort and safety. Some days I think Evelyn is content here but she has her moments: "This place is so small, I have to go outside to change my mind."

The other thing that was critical with my Mom's situation was to not discuss the matter of moving ahead of time. The very mention of this topic annoyed her a lot.

And finally, as mentioned earlier, home and kitchen have been a very important part of Mom's life. Although she can no longer do the cooking, baking, and canning, I find that when I ask her for helpful suggestions, this is empowering for her. The other evening when we chatted, I said, "Mother, I am canning cherries, I don't know how long to cook them." "Oh," laughed Evelyn. "That's easy, just cook them for 10 minutes, make sure they are well washed and your jars are clean, dear." This bit of advice-giving seemed to cheer her up.

Analysis

Home represents a place of safety, security and comfort. In this story, home has also been a place where Evelyn has been in charge and control of her life. Transition is one of the most difficult times in the journey, not being quite certain if it is the right time to move. How can this family maintain both the safety and security for Evelyn, while also allowing her independence?

Caring from a distance can prove to be extremely challenging. As with the daughter in the Apple Pie story (Chapter 10), this daughter truly believes that her mother's need to maintain independence and a sense of control by far outweighs the safety issues of moving her closer by. Keeping her as independent for as long as possible helps to outweigh the worry.

How can one know that their loved one is safe, and yet, at the same time empower the individual to keep them as independent as possible? One thing, which assisted a great deal in this transition, was to keep as many things the same as possible in Evelyn's environment. This continuity was empowering by allowing her control and choices. Also, the simplicity of the environment helps assure her safety.

The other important thing to consider about Evelyn is the continuing deterioration of her eyesight. It is critical to keep the environment as simple and uncluttered as possible, in order that Evelyn can safely navigate her way around. Being a haven of safety and security, home has been defined, in one sense, as the place where we can close our eyes, and walk around, finding everything we need without opening our eyes. At Wildflower Manor, Evelyn knows exactly where all her things are.

Finally, when families realize that the person's judgment may be impaired, or as in Evelyn's case, her vision is impaired, it is critical to have supports in place. In this story, the family has assured that Evelyn is connected to the Lifeline, her rooms are free of clutter, there are no loose scatter rugs that she may trip on, and the stove has been disconnected. This daughter stays in touch by telephone every other day, and Evelyn's good friend is close by to assure that various needs are met.

This family has had a transition in thinking as they realize, "I think my mother is trying to tell us something, and I think it's going to be alright."

What Works
• Simplify environment
• Empower Evelyn
• Assure that supports are in place

What Doesn't Work
• Bossing, telling Evelyn what she can and cannot do
• Discussing the move ahead of time
• Cluttered environment

Suggested Readings

Brackey, Jolene (2000). *Creating Moments of Joy: for the Person with Alzheimer's or Dementia.* Purdue

Olson, Arthur (1992). *The Dying of the Light: Living with Alzheimer's Disease. The General Store Publishing House,* Inc.

Powers, Bethel Ann (2003). *Nursing Home Ethics: Everyday Issues Affecting Residents with Dementia. Springer Publishing Company*

Silin, Peter S. (2001). *Nursing Homes: The Family's Journey.* Johns Hopkins University Press

Phase 4

Trust

the person still remains

The dictionary defines trust as "to commit or place in one's care or keeping." This is exactly what happens when the family brings the person with dementia to the nursing home. They are "trusting" that the professional caregivers will care for their loved one. On the other hand, the professional caregiver "trusts" that the family will share information about their loved one, so they can do their job properly. And, most importantly, the person with dementia "trusts" that he/she will receive care and understanding.

Family members have expressed "that they expect professional caregivers to be an extension of their own arm" in the care of their loved one. Some families have great difficulty in trusting that this will happen. When they arrive for a visit at the nursing home, Dad is holding hands with another female resident, or Mom is dressed in the same blue sweat suit as the other males and females living there. Even with these circumstances, families need to trust that their loved one is still "in there."

A daughter reports, "I have a great attachment to my memories with my mother. Since the diagnosis of Mom's Alzheimer's disease, she can no longer remember, so we are making new memories each day."

The person with dementia is down to the very basics—living in the moment. Receiving care and understanding makes them happy. Enjoying a chocolate ice cream cone makes them happy. Even their present diagnosis has not altered their preference for a favorite treat. And although this person may no longer have their memories of years past, the family must trust that their loved one's "personhood" remains intact.

These stories about trust bring to life the people who are living through dementia. It is very liberating for family members when they join the loved one with dementia in their journey.

This phase will assist family and professional caregivers in understanding the journey. First, the true story will be revealed of the shared lived experience, followed by an interview with the caregiver to identify creative coping strategies, and finally there will be an analysis of the situation that can empower both the caregiver and the person with dementia. Caregivers will discover what works (and what does not) for each unique situation.

16

She Wanted Two Kisses

this spouse shares creative solutions of learning to speak Alzheimer's

*R*ose sits in the lounge chair. The morning rays of sunlight shine on her face, illuminating her once bright, blue eyes. A person greets her, "Good morning Rose." Rose does not respond and she does not recognize the person who is greeting her.

Morning follows morning, day follows day for Rose at Memory Care Manor. Family photographs hang on the wall, persistent of a memory long ago. Rose sits waiting for a long time for Jack, her husband, who is coming for a visit. And when he enters the lounge, prepared to assist his wife with her breakfast, Rose displays no apparent recognition of him.

Rose remains motionless, eyes fixated. This could mean that she no longer knows her husband. Or it could mean that she does not wish to violate the etiquette of Memory Care Manor with an enthusiastic greeting, which may be interpreted by some as inappropriate. Or it could mean, for Rose, that the acceptable response to a "good morning" from Jack is a dead-eyed stare.

However, Jack finds encouragement in this lack of reaction. He continues to prepare Rose to eat her breakfast. Jack is not surprised. He knows that Rose has Alzheimer's disease. What Jack does not comprehend is why his darling wife of 57 years no longer speaks to him.

Jack lives close to Memory Care Manor. This day, following his visit with Rose, Jack visits the public library. He has decided to tackle head-on, his own research of learning about Alzheimer's disease. From his reading at the library, Jack learns that in 1906, Dr. Alois Alzheimer examined a slice of brain tissue under the microscope, identifying plaques and tangles surrounding the brain cells, a hallmark of Alzheimer's disease. As a result, there may be mental deterioration. Jack learned that the person affected, his Rose, may no longer be able to communicate as she previously could. Due to the brain tissue deterioration, the language center of the brain may be affected. Consequently, the person has difficulty understanding, or being understood. Jack begins to realize that Rose is doing the best she can.

The next morning, Jack arrives early at Memory Care Manor, armed and ready with his new-found knowledge. Rose sits in her familiar place in the corner of the lounge at Memory Care Manor, motionless, waiting, waiting, waiting.

When Jack enters the room with a cheery "good morning," he makes a special point of warmly embracing his wife. He then asks the caregiver if they might play a soft piece of classical music (Rose's favorite) on the stereo. Jack moves Rose's lounge chair to a quieter corner of the lounge, removed from other noises and distractions. He then brings Rose's breakfast tray and sits with her, preparing to feed her breakfast.

"Here my Rose, have some porridge," says Jack, offering a spoonful to Rose's lips. No reaction. This does not discourage Jack. He takes Rose's hand and holds it, as he offers a second spoonful of porridge. This time, Jack notes a special little smile around Rose's mouth as she swallows the cereal and that her body language is more relaxed. She is listening to the classical music softly playing in the background.

Jack leans forward, closer to Rose and says, "Does my Rose still love me?" At first, no response. And then, Rose also leans forward, puckering up her lips for a kiss. Jack responds in kind with a kiss. Once again, Rose puckers up her lips and leans forward. Jack smiles and says, "My Rose wants two kisses."

The interview with Jack, the husband follows:

1 **Jack, when did you first notice that something might be wrong with Rose?**

It was a gradual thing. Rose had short-term memory loss and this was distressing for her. She couldn't seem to remember from one minute to the next what she had or hadn't done. She would tell our daughter about something that had happened, and then five minutes later, she would re-tell the same story.

2 **It is interesting that in spite of the fact that Rose does not speak to you, you still remain so positive. Could you comment on that?**

I can see her brightness vanishing, but I love Rose because she is so loveable. Nothing can ever change that. Not even Alzheimer's disease. I believe that Rose's spirit is alive and well, in spite of it all. This keeps me going.

3   **You mentioned she gave a special little smile that morning. What do you think she was thinking?**

Rose and I met on Valentine's Day. That same piece of classical music was playing when we met. And that morning when the staff played the music, and I saw Rose's little smile, I really believe that she is remembering too.

4   **When Rose sits there in her chair, present but distant, you must feel wistful for days gone by. Do you want to talk about those feelings?**

Well, yes, I'm pretty attached to my memories with Rose. We've been married for 57 years. That's a lot of years and a lot of memories. I guess though, I'm coming to a place where I feel like Rose and I can still have a life without those memories. I know that sounds kinda strange, but I tell the kids, "Mom and I are making new memories every day."

5   **Jack, how do you handle it when Rose no longer recognizes you?**

It makes me sad. I tell myself, this disease is not about me. But I can't help my feelings. Rose has always been so vibrant and alive and chatty. These days she is in her own little world.

6   **You mentioned you had done some research on the subject at the public library. Was this information useful for you?**

I'll say. I was reading about the mental deterioration and the fact that the brain size is actually shrinking. And I read that there are plaques and tangles surrounding the nerve cells of the brain. I understand that the language centre of Rose's brain may be affected, and this is why she no longer speaks. I mentioned before that I believe Rose's spirit is alive and well, in spite of Alzheimer's. I believe my Rose is still in there, and when she doesn't speak, I think she is swallowing her feelings.

7 **How do you deal with the silence?**

I now understand that Rose is doing the best she can. It's hard sometimes because I'll be talking to Rose about a memory or something we've done together with the family, and I pause, waiting for Rose to respond like she always has. And there's silence. That's hard to take.

8 **What are some of Rose's favorite things? And is she still able to enjoy those things?**

Rose always has had incredible energy and creativity. She spent countless hours with the children—of course, she enjoyed being a mother. But Rose was very involved in community and school committees. And she loved to entertain. Rose was always busy helping others. Today, Rose still loves having people around her. And she enjoys listening to stories.

9 **Let's talk about you for a moment Jack. What things do you do to take care of yourself?**

I read a lot. And I enjoy walking. I'm here at Rose's side every day, and when the weather warms up, I'll take Rose outside to the garden. We always enjoyed walking in the garden together. I still do.

10 **What did you feel in that moment when Rose puckered up for a kiss?**

Our eyes connected briefly just before that kiss, and I thought to myself, "I've got my Rose back once again."

I was so astonished, I hugged her and said, "We really do love one another, don't we Rose?"

11 **Your journey with Rose has encouraged so many other people in similar situations. What do you tell them when they are angry about the situation?**

I tell them that there is help and—just as important— that there is hope. I haven't worked it all out yet. I'm struggling. But on the good days, I know that this Alzheimer's disease has happened to my Rose for a reason. And I'm grateful that we have this time together.

Analysis

Communicating with the person with dementia can prove to be one of the greatest challenges. These individuals may no longer communicate with words but with feelings. Because feelings are not often well communicated (message not received or understood), frustration can run high, both for the person with dementia and their caregiver. The person with dementia may not be able to express themselves or even complete a simple sentence and so more feeling-based and intuitive means of communication are required.

Jack truly believes that Rose's spirit is alive and well. Believing this is often the only hope that families can hang on to.

When caregivers face this situation, they need to first assess who this person is. Although the individual may not be speaking, his or her body language is alive with feelings. You can see by watching whether the person is sad, or moving in an agitated manner. You can read emotions by watching their eyes—eyes are the "windows to the soul." Jack has learned to read in Rose's eyes what she's trying to say, and he tries to interpret her body language. Jack discovered that he needs to pay particular attention to the meaning of Rose's facial expressions, as he notes "a special little smile around Rose's mouth . . ."

A large part of communicating with anyone is related to "the knowing" about who this person was prior to the dementia. Jack knows that Rose loves classical music. He knows about her personhood, and her sense of self. When caregivers have this information, they are then able to acknowledge who Rose is, and understand her emotions so much better. This enhances the communication process, empowering both the caregiver and the person.

What Works:
- Using a gentle touch
- Understanding body language
- Knowing the person is doing the best they can
- Providing a quiet environment

What Doesn't Work:
- Noisy environment
- Rushing the person
- Talking about the person in front of them

17

Dorothy

this robin sings for her breakfast

*I*t is breakfast time at Tick Tock Manor. However, Dorothy is not eating breakfast. Dorothy is doing her toddler shuffle, pacing up and down the long hallways of the Manor. This behavior has been going on for many weeks. The caregivers are becoming concerned about Dorothy; she has lost interest in food and is losing weight.

The caregiver, Jenny, approaches Dorothy as she is pacing.

"Dorothy, how are you this morning?"

Dorothy stares straight ahead without responding.

"Dorothy, may I walk with you?" asks Jenny.

"Alright," Dorothy says.

Walking along for a little while, Jenny leads Dorothy to a quiet spot away from the noise of the dining room. Here she has placed Dorothy's breakfast and a cup of tea, with a little milk, prepared just the way she likes it.

"Dorothy, isn't this lovely? Here is your breakfast that I've prepared for you."

No response from Dorothy.

Jenny has also brought along a "bird book" that makes bird songs. "Listen to this robin, Dorothy," she says, as she pushes a button and the robin sings. Dorothy is now alert and paying attention to the bird sounds.

As time passes, Dorothy begins eating her breakfast. Jenny continues to sit with her and to play the different bird songs. Then something happens which really surprises Jenny.

Dorothy says, "When I was a little girl, my mother would take me to the park and we would sit together on the park bench and listen to the birds singing. That bird book just makes me remember the time with my mother."

"I am delighted Dorothy," responds Jenny, and they enjoy this nice moment together. Birds sing as Dorothy continues to munch on her toast and sip her tea.

Just about every day now at Tick Tock Manor, you will see Dorothy doing her toddler shuffle, up and down the long corridor. But now she pauses for breakfast.

The interview with Jenny, Dorothy's caregiver follows:

1   **You seem to have a lovely sense of "knowing" about Dorothy. Have you cared for her for some time?**

Yes indeed, I've cared for her for quite some time. Dorothy has been living at Tick Tock Manor for seven years. I can remember when she first came here, she would jump out of bed in the morning, and couldn't wait to get down to breakfast. Dorothy would say, "I like my breakfast best, because at breakfast time I know exactly what I'm getting. I have rice cereal, a banana, one piece of toast with jam, and a cup of tea. At the other mealtimes, there may be sauces and spices and I don't trust what I am getting, but at breakfast time I do."

2   **What is your perception of the current situation with Dorothy losing interest in mealtimes?**

Dorothy's behavior is very different lately. She no longer seems to recognize the need for hunger and thirst. We are concerned about her weight loss.

3   **It sounds like Dorothy is firm about her likes and dislikes.**

You are right; Dorothy knows exactly what she wants. And it takes her a little while before she gets to know her caregivers and to trust them.

4   **What is your game plan for building trust and encouraging Dorothy to eat?**

We have partnered with Dorothy's family to find out as much as we can about her. We ask about her likes and dislikes at mealtimes and hope to discover some special things about Dorothy as a person, you know, the way she was before she became a resident here at Tick Tock Manor.

5   **What lessons have you learned from this partnering?**

I've learned that Dorothy has always valued her time for quiet and solitude, which is the reason we have created a quiet breakfast spot for Dorothy. Just this one piece of information has been extremely helpful in planning Dorothy's care. Her family has shared that Dorothy has been an avid gardener and nature lover for many years. Dorothy and her husband enjoyed bird watching.

6 **Do you expect better results now with Dorothy's care?**

I feel encouraged with using the "bird book." It takes some time to develop trust. As we join Dorothy in her reality she becomes less resistant to care. She is trusting that we will deliver care and understanding for her.

7 **Any final comments?**

Only that Dorothy is living in the moment; receiving care and understanding makes her happy. I love to see her face light up when I spend time with her.

Analysis

Down the long hallways of Tick Tock Manor walks Dorothy. And she walks and walks and walks. This pacing behavior is typical of persons with dementia. Due to mental deterioration the individual with dementia perseveres with walking, and forgets to eat and drink. Only the caregivers are distressed about this, not Dorothy.

Naturally, because Dorothy spends so much time in her day pacing, she does not take the time to eat. As a result, she is losing weight (as with Bob in Chapter 3). Trust is the phase of the journey when weight loss and dehydration become a concern.

Communicating with Dorothy and trying to convince her to take a time out for breakfast is proving to be a challenge. She no longer communicates with words but with feelings. Her body language expresses agitation and because of this, frustration levels can run high for both the person with dementia and his or her caregiver. The noisy dining room provides sensory overload for Dorothy; creating a quiet breakfast spot for Dorothy is a wise move.

When faced with such situations, caregivers first need to assess the person's likes and dislikes and to watch for body-language clues. It is evident that Jenny knows something about Dorothy's biography and is aware that Dorothy enjoys nature as well as solitude while eating.

The next step is to join the person on their journey and enter their world. This can prove challenging with Dorothy because she does not respond much. However, Jenny has brought along a tool to begin this communication process—the book that produces bird songs. "Listen to this robin, Dorothy," she says as she pushes the button and the robin sings.

The book of bird sounds and similar tools can be purchased at most bookstores in the children's department. It not only provides excellent distraction for the person who may otherwise be agitated, but also helps establish trust.

People with dementia live in the moment; receiving care and understanding makes them happy. Enjoying the bird songs makes them happy, as does reminiscing about childhood.

Encouraging better eating habits for Dorothy and meeting her nutritional needs are very important, so caregivers must first create a climate of trust with Dorothy. The robin singing helps to build this trust.

What Works:
- Joining Dorothy on her walk
- Understanding the person's body language
- Knowing the person
- Using a communication tool, such as the bird-sound book

What Doesn't Work:
- Noisy environment
- Forcing Dorothy to sit for long periods
- Rushing the person

18

Bathing Sparky

a dog provides creative solutions for bathing a person with dementia

*P*eter was 13 when he had his first dog, 18 when he worked in the lumber camps, and 20 when he married. Now 74, Peter is pacing up and down the hallways of Tick Tock Manor where he is a resident. Peter always paces on this day, because today is Peter's bath day.

Things are done right on schedule at Tick Tock Manor. The caregivers never forget Peter's bath day. It's interesting that, although Peter has dementia, he never forgets the bath day either.

This morning is different, however. Peter is clutching a small book close to his chest. When the caregiver approaches him to offer to assist Peter with his bath, he becomes agitated and walks off quickly in the other direction. Any further mention of bathing sets Peter off in an angry outburst.

When I approach Peter and ask if he would like to share

what is in his book, Peter continues walking off in the opposite direction. He then pauses to think, places his hand on his hip, and replies, "Sure, why not?"

Peter and I sit side by side in the lounge next to the bathing area. He opens a small family photo album, eager to show me some pictures. Many of the photos are of a black Labrador dog in a garden.

"Who is this Peter?" I ask.

"That's Sparky, my dog," replies Peter, with a big smile on his face. Peter is happy to share that he and his dog Sparky have spent many happy years together. He also adds that he misses Sparky very much. In one of the photos, Peter is in the backyard with Sparky, giving the dog a bath.

"What's going on in this picture Peter?" I ask.

"Oh, Sparky is having his summer bath," says Peter. "I can't do the bath in the house, because Sparky races around after, shaking off all the water. Sparky loves being clean." Peter shows pride on his face.

I see this as an opportunity to distract Peter away from his own bathing issues.

"Peter, you and Sparky sure have had a lot of fun together. And Sparky likes to be nice and fresh and clean. That's great. Let me help you to be nice and clean as well. And when Sparky comes for a visit, you will be fresh. How does that sound?"

"I don't know about that. Do you think my wife can bring Sparky for a visit?"

"Sure she can Peter, anytime, and you and Sparky can have a good visit. But first let me help you with your bath. Let's go."

"Oh, alright," says Peter. He takes my hand and we walk together to the bathing area.

The small photo album is left behind on the table, the photos holding memories of who Peter was, and his best friend, Sparky.

Interview with Peter's caregiver follows:

1 **What seem to be the main obstacles in giving Peter his bath?**

Just about everything. Peter doesn't like taking his clothes off. He doesn't like having his hair washed, or getting wet. When Peter is finished his bath he wants to put the same clothes right back on. He gets really angry with us if we try to persuade him otherwise.

2 **What suggestions or alternatives have you tried so far?**

We no longer wash Peter's hair on bath day. Rather, his hair is shampooed in the salon where the hair cuts are done. Also, the girls on the last shift lay out fresh clothes for Peter in the morning so that the clothes Peter insists on putting on after his bath are clean.

3 **How is this working?**

Good. Peter is far less agitated.

4 **I understand Peter has a dog, Sparky. Does Peter ever talk about his dog?**

To be honest, I didn't know that Peter even had a dog. That is really good information for us. Maybe we can ask the family to bring the dog in for a visit.

5 **That is a great idea, Peter would love that. Also, does Peter ever speak of the days he worked in the lumber camps?**

Yes, now that you mention it, Peter loves to reminisce about those days. He's told me he feels lucky that he didn't lose a finger when he was working in the lumber camps. And he says, "Those were the best days of my life."

6   **Can you offer suggestions for other caregivers having similar difficulties?**

The most helpful thing I have discovered is to never argue with the person with dementia, or to try to get them to do something they don't want to do. Rather, I allow time for Peter, and perhaps try again twenty minutes later.

7   **Do Peter's family visit often? Do you think they might have some suggestions about the bathing time?**

I see his wife come just about every day to see Peter. I never thought to ask her about Peter's bath, but now that you mention it, I bet she would have some helpful suggestions.

8   **Does the family visit make any difference to Peter's behavior?**

During the time his wife is here, Peter is happy. However, when she leaves, Peter starts pacing again. I think he's lonely.

9   **Overall, what is your perception of the present situation?**

I've learned to never rush Peter, and to avoid arguing with him. No means no. When Peter gets agitated, and feels that we are trying to rush him, he will say, "Don't guess, wait till my mind tells me." He wants us to know that he is still the one in charge.

Analysis

Bathing time can be one of the most challenging times for the caregiver, and one of the most frightening times for the person with dementia. Think of all the steps we ourselves need to take when preparing for a bath.

First, we need to be organized enough to gather all of our supplies and draw the water. Then we must undress, and for Peter that is uncomfortable because he does not like taking off his clothes in front of another person. Most people do not like feeling chilled. Persons with dementia especially do not like being cold.

Then, actually getting into the water can be very frightening for persons with dementia. They may feel out of control or that they could drown. After bathing, it's yet another adjustment to get out of the nice warm water and then to use the dry towel. Next is the fuss of finding clean clothes and getting dressed.

In terms of everyday function, Peter is down to the very basics. He lives in the moment. Talking about his dog, Sparky, makes him happy as does reminiscing about the days of working in the lumber camps. Peter is not interested in bathing and (as with Alfred in Chapter 9), is resistant to care. He sees no reason for taking a bath. In fact, any discussion over three minutes is too long to even discuss the bath. The caregiver needs to change the subject and discuss what makes Peter happy.

Family caregivers have brought their loved one to the nursing home, and trust that the professional caregivers will provide care and understanding. Professional caregivers trust that the family will share information with them about their loved one. And the person with dementia trusts that they will receive care and understanding.

What Works:
- Discussing a topic of interest
- Keeping the person warm
- Utilizing distraction

What Doesn't Work:
- Discussing the bath
- Rushing the person with dementia
- Allowing the person to become chilled

19

Sisters Again

she remembers the pet rabbits

Elsie is walking down the dark hallway of Lavender Lane, where she lives. It is 6:00 a.m. and Elsie looks lost and confused. She is wearing her warm, flannelette white-and-blue poodle pajamas and looking for her pet rabbit.

"Where's my rabbit? Have you seen my rabbit?" Elsie asks no one in particular. "When you see my rabbit please put him up on the counter, I miss him." As children, Elsie and her sister Ada, had pet rabbits.

Lily, Elsie's caregiver, brings her the wheelchair. Elsie sits down, and then Lily pushes her the remainder of the way down the hallway. Elsie now sits by the nurses' station.

"Oh," says Elsie, looking over her shoulder to see Lily, "I knew there was someone there."

Ada and Elsie are sisters. They both live in Lavender Lane nursing home. However, they do not know it. That is, they do not know they live there and they do not realize that the other sister lives so close by. This is because Ada is in late-stage Alzheimer's disease, and her sister, Elsie has dementia and is deaf as well. One day Lily has an inspiration to bring these sisters together.

Elsie has suffered a stroke and generally feels confused. Due to her deafness, she uses a "pocket talker" to assist in communication. Similar to a microphone with earplugs, the pocket talker device enables Elsie to hear the speaker and join in the conversation.

Ada remains in bed, curled up in the fetal position. And while she appears to be comfortable, she is not responding.

Lily brings Elsie in her wheelchair to Ada's bedside. She then places the ear plugs for the pocket talker into Elsie's ears and explains to Elsie that her sister, Ada, is lying in the bed waiting to have a visit with her.

"She won't speak to me," says Elsie. "Are you sleeping Ada? Yoo, hoooo!"

Lily pushes Elsie a little closer to Ada's side. Ada remains unresponsive.

However, the two sisters are now holding hands. Ada does not speak but she begins stroking Elsie's hand. Lily leaves the room and the two sisters continue to share this special moment.

"We used to have lots of fun, Ada," says Elsie. "And that is the picture I gave you," she adds, pointing up at the wall at a picture of a butterfly.

This has been a very special visit for these two sisters. On the very next day, Elsie dies quietly in her sleep. Ada does not realize, but she seems happier and smiles as she remembers the pet rabbits.

A niece is visiting from out of town; the interview follows:

1   My sympathy to you and your family on the passing of Elsie. When Ada and Elsie were young, did they have pet rabbits?

Thank you for your sympathy. Yes, they had rabbits and also dogs, cats, hamsters, and chickens. They both loved animals. Elsie, especially took care of the animals, and took care of Ada as well.

2   Talk about your relationship with your Aunties when you were growing up.

Aunt Elsie was like a Mother to me. She left behind a legacy of fun and laughter. Whenever I visited my aunties, we had fun and games. I have a great attachment to these memories with my aunts. It has hurt so much to visit them at Lavender Lane, and they no longer can communicate with me.

3   When the sisters were together they seemed very happy, talking about their growing-up years.

As girls, my aunts did everything together; apparently they were almost inseparable. Ada wouldn't play outside without Elsie. They would play hopscotch, skip, and enjoy hide-and-seek. Elsie protected Ada. Now that Elsie is gone, I'm the only one Ada has left.

4   I saw the beautiful needlepoint butterfly picture that Elsie made. Can you tell me about some of the other things that Elsie would do for her sister, Ada?

Yes, Elsie did make the butterfly picture for Ada, but the girls did the sewing and needlepoint together. They played the piano together; Elsie always let Ada play first. Ada tended to be shy, so Elsie always would encourage her. They enjoyed cooking, gardening, and they did everything together.

5   **Do the other caregivers know something of the family history of Ada and Elsie? Do you think it makes a difference to their care?**

I visit once or twice a week. It seems that when caregivers who know my aunties were caring for them, Ada and Elsie were calmer. I suppose that's because they relate to them as unique individuals.

6   **What is your perception of the current situation?**

Even though Ada may not realize that Elsie has passed, she will feel the loss. She will need extra caring and understanding. There was a trust between the two sisters that will last forever.

Analysis

What is Elsie doing? She is walking up and down the long, dark hallways of Lavender Lane, looking lost and confused. What is she looking for? Elsie is looking for her pet rabbit. As she becomes more and more demented, the childhood memories become clearer and more prominent in her mind.

Communicating with Elsie can prove very challenging for the caregivers. Not only is she deaf, but she is convinced that her pet rabbits are here at Lavender Lane. In dementia care there may be one journey, but there are two different paths and two different realities—the path of the person with dementia is a much different reality than that of her caregivers. Elsie's reality is that she is a child playing with her sister Ada, and their pet rabbits.

The first step for the caregiver is to join Elsie on her path and enter her reality. When the caregiver brings Elsie to Ada's bedside, she activates a special moment for the sisters together. Using the pocket talker, the sisters are able to enjoy their conversation. Perhaps, they are even reminiscing about their childhood memories with their pet rabbits.

Trust is defined as "to commit or place in one's care or keeping." The family trusts that their loved one will be cared for; family caregivers have reported that they trust the professional to become an extension of their own arm. The professional caregivers trust that the family will share invaluable information with them so they can do their job as effectively as possible. The person with dementia at some level trusts that he or she will receive care and understanding. Family members trust that when the disease is lifted, the person remains.

What Works:
- Joining the sisters in their reality
- Facilitating soft touch (e.g. holding hands)
- Knowing the person
- Using a communication device such as the pocket talker

What Doesn't Work:
- Reality orientation (the pet rabbit no longer lives here)
- Noisy environment
- Rushing the person

Suggested Readings

Bell, Virginia & Troxel, David (2001). *The Best Friends Staff: Building a Culture of Care in Alzheimer's Programs.* Health Professions Press, Inc.

Castleman, Michael, et al. (2000). *There's Still a Person in There: The Complete Guide to Treating and Coping with Alzheimer's.* G.P. Putnam's Sons.

Coste, Joanne Koenig (2003). *Learning to Speak Alzheimer's: A Groundbreaking Approach for Everyone Dealing with the Disease.* Houghton Mifflin.

Everett, Deborah (1996). *Forget Me Not: The Spiritual Care of People with Alzheimer's.* Inkwell Press.

Strauss, Claudia J. (2002). *Talking to Alzheimer's: Simple Ways to Connect When You Visit with a Family Member or Friend.* New Harbinger Publications.

Identify
The Phase

How To Use These Case Studies

*T*he following case studies are shared lived experiences. They are based on true stories; only the names and places have been changed. These stories illustrate the different phases of the dementia journey: Turmoil, Transformation, Transition, and Trust. However, there is no interview and no analysis provided in this section. As a learning tool, the reader is invited to identify the phase, using the checklist format. I have found this process to be extremely successful in so many of my workshops. Learners discover caring solutions that they had not even thought of.

Family members are trying so hard to understand and make some sense of the phase their loved one is passing through. This section of the Living Dementia Approach invites the reader to identify the phase that best describe their present situation in caring for a loved one or a resident with dementia.

153

A daughter said: "Mother was always the strong one. She was always there for the family. Now, she no longer recognizes any of us."

This daughter needs to understand how long these symptoms will last, so that she can plan for the next phase of the journey. This section of the Living Dementia Approach invites the reader to identify the phase. In so doing, the individual may discover which phase they are going through.

Read each of the following stories, then identify the phase that best applies: Turmoil, Transformation, Transition, or Trust.

Note: some case studies may reveal more than one phase.

Florence

*F*lorence does not want to go to bed. In fact, Florence is dressing up and putting her coat on. The more the caregiver attempts to encourage Florence to undress and get ready for bed, the more agitated and angry Florence becomes.

As we explore different strategies for settling Florence to bed for the night, it becomes increasingly evident that she is not going to do what is required. Is she in pain? Is she hungry? Does she need to go to the bathroom? Florence definitely follows her own mind. One thing that the caregiver discovers is that Florence is chilly, and actually needs an extra blanket on her bed. When this is offered, she soon drifts off to sleep. The fact that persons with dementia get easily chilled, is supported by the literature (see Transformation; Suggested Readings; Brackey, 2000). Florence was putting on her coat because she was cold.

Identify the phase that applies to the above story:
- ☐ Turmoil
- ☐ Transformation
- ☐ Transition
- ☐ Trust

Hint: see Chapter 11, "Kay" and Chapter 17, "Dorothy" for what works and what doesn't.

155

Eleanor

*E*leanor is a resident at Tick Tock Manor. She has been diagnosed as being in the early to middle-stage of Alzheimer's disease and has a hearing impairment. Eleanor's caregiver, Anne, has entered the room to assist Eleanor to get ready for breakfast. Anne has been caring for Eleanor for three years. The time is 7:15 a.m.; things are done right on time at Tick Tock Manor.

"Good morning Eleanor," says Anne. "I will help you to get ready for breakfast."

"Who are you? I've never seen you before in my life," Eleanor responds.

"My name is Anne, and I will assist you to get ready," she says.

"When did I start needing help? I'm not sure what is going on here. Do you know what is going on?" Eleanor asks.

"It's alright if you don't remember; I will help you," replies Anne.

"NO, it's NOT alright," Eleanor is angry now. "It's NOT alright; I seem to be losing my mind. Go away; I don't know who you are, I don't know where I am," she says, "and it's far too early for visitors."

At this point, Anne chooses to take a "time-out" and allow Eleanor some space and time to be alone and rest a little while longer.

Identify the phase that applies to the above story:
- ☐ Turmoil
- ☐ Transformation
- ☐ Transition
- ☐ Trust

Hint: see Chapter 18, "Bathing Sparky" for what works and what doesn't.

Barbara

Frank is devoted to Barbara; they have been married for 57 years. Since the diagnosis of Alzheimer's disease and her recent fall, Barbara has been admitted to the nursing home where she now lives. Frank visits every day.

Not only is Frank devoted to Barbara, he adores her. He has built his whole life around their relationship, and now his life revolves around caring for her in the nursing home where Barbara now resides.

Some days, when Frank arrives for a visit, he discovers that the brief that Barbara is wearing is very wet and requires changing. Frank is only concerned for the comfort of his wife and becomes annoyed with the caregivers when this happens.

However, when Frank brings this up to the nursing staff, the caregivers become defensive and bring up several reasons why this is occurring.

What should Frank do?

Identify the phase that applies to the above story:
- ☐ Turmoil
- ☐ Transformation
- ☐ Transition
- ☐ Trust

Hint: see Chapter 3, "One Shoe On" for what works and what doesn't.

Harold

*I*t's 4:00 p.m. at Tick Tock Manor where Harold lives. Harold has dementia of the Alzheimer's type and he is hungry. Dinner will be served by the care staff at 5:30 p.m.; everything is done on time here at Tick Tock Manor. There is no change of schedule here.

Harold is so hungry that he keeps asking the nurses, "Is it dinner time yet? Is it dinner time yet?"

Harold and others with the same condition may have no sense of time. Harold may say he is hungry, or he may not even recognize the sensations of hunger or thirst. In this situation, Harold's hunger is triggered by the fact that he can smell the dinner cooking.

The caregiver has a busy schedule and she is beginning to feel annoyed. In order to satisfy Harold's hunger and to stop his constant request for dinner ahead of schedule, she decides to prepare a small cheese sandwich for Harold. She thinks this will not spoil his appetite for dinner, and also will prevent repeated queries about dinner.

Harold quickly ate up the sandwich, wiped the crumbs from his lip, looked at the nurse and asked, "Is it dinner time yet?"

Identify the phase that applies to the above story:
- ☐ Turmoil
- ☐ Transformation
- ☐ Transition
- ☐ Trust

Hint: see Chapter 2, "Wheelchair Ballet" for what works and what doesn't.

George

When the family can no longer care for George at home, he is admitted to Memory Care Manor, a unit specially designed for persons with dementia.

Mary, the nurse is attempting to give George his morning medication. He is being quite resistant. In fact, George flatly refuses to take the medication.

"George, if you are in a combative mood, I want you to lie down and I will cover you with a nice warm blanket," says Mary.

"I want to get warmed up first, that's what I want," says George. "I want some peace; I don't want anymore pills."

"Alright, George, I will leave you alone," responds Mary. She honors George's wishes, covers him with a blanket, and leaves the room.

That afternoon, George, and his wife, Margaret, are sitting in the lounge at Memory Care Manor. The music therapist is sitting in the centre of the circle playing her guitar.

George's toe is tapping to the music of the guitar. Margaret's arm is lightly touching George's shoulder, her fingers tapping on his back to the rhythm of the music.

George says, "I like the feel of your hand there."

Margaret responds, "I am glad George," and they continue enjoying the moment together.

Identify the phase that applies to the above story:
- ☐ Turmoil
- ☐ Transformation
- ☐ Transition
- ☐ Trust

Hint: see Chapter 16, "She Wanted Two Kisses" for what works and what doesn't.

Margaret

*M*argaret's caregiver cannot encourage her to get up this morning. It is already 7:45 a.m. and breakfast is being served at 8:00 a.m.

"What are you girls doing in my home?" says Margaret. "This is my home."

"How come all of you are here?" she persists. "I'm going back to Ireland if you don't leave."

"Who are you coming into my home?" she asks. "And where are my teeth? I think I've swallowed them." Margaret has a frown on her face.

"I'm staying in bed today," says Margaret, her voice now is softer.

"Margaret, what kind of juice would you like?" asks Shirley, the caregiver (changing the subject).

"I like anything that doesn't talk back to me," replies Margaret. "Where do you think we got our noses from?"

"I'm not sure," said Shirley. "I think perhaps, from our mothers."

Margaret says, "My nose is so big, I can nearly stir my tea with it."

Identify the phase that applies to the above story:

- ☐ Turmoil
- ☐ Transformation
- ☐ Transition
- ☐ Trust

Hint: see Chapter 9, "Alfred" for what works and what doesn't.

Ann

*A*nn lives at Amber Lane Manor. She is diagnosed with middle-stage Alzheimer's disease. When her caregiver Liza enters the lounge, Ann is sitting with her legs crossed; one shoe and one sock have been removed. She is wearing this sock on her left hand.

Liza greets Ann, "Good morning Ann, how are you to-day?"

"This is my Father," responds Ann, as she introduces her "socked hand."

"Hello," says Liza to the socked hand. "How are you do-ing?"

"This is the program," Ann replies.

"I understand, and what is it about?" asks Liza.

"The seven children," says Ann.

Communicating with persons with dementia can be very interesting and challenging. As in the above situation, the con-versation may make little sense. However to the person with dementing illness, they feel there is a real context and meaning to what they are saying.

Following breakfast, Liza finds Ann pacing the long hall-way of Amber Lane Manor. Ann only has one shoe on. Liza joins her on her journey.

"Good morning Ann. How is your daughter, Sarah?" It was

mentioned in the morning report that Ann's daughter had just visited.

Ann responds, "The program is this way or the program is that way."

"Sarah loves you very much," replies Liza.

Ann now points at a painting of horses on the wall. "I see the dogs walking," says Ann.

"Oh yes, what nice dogs," responds Liza, going along with Ann's interpretation of the painting. "Let's walk along with the dogs."

"I love Sarah too," says Ann, smiling happily.

As Alzheimer's disease progresses, caregivers may need to use more nonverbal communication methods such as touching or hugging. But in the above illustration, Liza was able to join Ann in her thoughts, causing Ann to reflect upon her visit with her daughter.

Identify the phase that applies to the above story:
- ☐ Turmoil
- ☐ Transformation
- ☐ Transition
- ☐ Trust

Hint: see Chapter 17, "Dorothy" for what works and what doesn't.

Catherine

Catherine has had a stroke and suffers from multi-infarct dementia. She is living at Memory Care Manor and is confined to the wheelchair. However, Catherine likes to "wheel" herself around the neighborhood of Memory Care Manor. Today she is holding the hand of Jenny, her caregiver, who is walking beside the wheelchair as Catherine is speaking. Due to her stroke, Catherine's speech is impaired. Jenny must listen very closely in order to understand what Catherine is saying.

"I don't know what's going on," says Catherine. "Nothing seems to make sense anymore."

"It will soon be dinnertime; are you hungry Catherine?" asks Jenny. "And I think your daughter will be coming for a visit. In fact, here she comes now."

Catherine looks up to see her daughter's smiling face there. "Hi Mom," says Rachel with a smile. Catherine now is crying tears of joy to see her daughter.

"Good to see you Mom," says Rachel, as she gives her mother a kiss. "Mom, we are going to be away for a little vacation; we will be gone for two weeks," the daughter shares with her Mom. This time, Catherine is not crying tears of joy, but real tears.

"You can't go away now; you never told me you were going away," cries Catherine. "What shall I do?"

Rachel is obviously distressed at her mother's reaction. "Mom, I told you we have been planning this trip for some time, and now we are going to be away for two weeks. I have left auntie's telephone number for the nurse to call if you should need anything."

Catherine continues weeping.

Identify the phase that applies to the above story:
- ☐ Turmoil
- ☐ Transformation
- ☐ Transition
- ☐ Trust

Hint: see Chapter 5, "Wish You Were Here" for what works and what doesn't.

Betty

Betty has lived a long time at Tick Tock Manor. Her son had been her primary caregiver for seven years prior to Betty's admission a few months ago. Betty suffers from osteoarthritis as well as osteoporosis and is in the middle-stage of Alzheimer's disease. Betty's arthritic pain is relieved by high doses of pain medication. When Betty's son was caring for his mother at home, he made sure that her medication was delivered right on schedule as he cared about his mother's comfort.

Today, when he comes for a visit, he discovers that Betty is weeping uncontrollably. The son asks the nurse if his mother has received her pain medication this morning.

"Oh no," the nurse responds. "The physician has discontinued all of Betty's medication; I haven't given her any."

The son is furious. He doesn't understand why his mother's medications have been stopped. Why has he not been included in this decision making? Why has the physician not consulted him? It breaks his heart to see his mother suffering. What should this son do?

Identify the phase that applies to the above story:
- ☐ Turmoil
- ☐ Transformation
- ☐ Transition
- ☐ Trust

Hint: this son needs to partner with the professional caregivers and trust that they are caring for his mother, Betty, as best they can.

Velma

Charles visits his wife Velma every day at Daisy Drive Manor where she lives. Now that Velma is diagnosed in late-stage Alzheimer's disease, she requires assistance with most of her activities of daily living, including mealtimes. Dealing with his own health challenges, Velma's care was becoming too much of a load for Charles to manage at home.

Charles really enjoys helping his wife at lunch and dinnertime. Why shouldn't he? Velma and Charles have been married for 57 years and she has been cooking meals for him all these years. Charles feels obligated to now assist his wife.

Due to health reasons, Charles no longer drives a car. His daughter drives him to the nursing home. Most days, when he arrives for a visit, Velma no longer recognizes Charles. She pushes the cup or spoon away when he attempts to feed her. And when Charles talks to Velma, she doesn't respond. Charles is becoming more and more concerned about Velma.

The next day, when lunch is being served to Velma, there is no sign of Charles. The caregivers are told that he will not be visiting today. Charles has had a heart attack.

Identify the phase that applies to the above story:
- ☐ Turmoil
- ☐ Transformation
- ☐ Transition
- ☐ Trust

Hint: see Chapter 16, "She Wanted Two Kisses" for what works and what doesn't.

Doris & Henry

*D*oris cared for her husband, Henry, for two years at home before he was admitted to the nursing home. Henry is diagnosed as being in the middle-stage of Alzheimer's disease. He has lived at Memory Care Manor for two years now. Most days Henry seems content.

Today, Doris has taken Henry out for a drive in their Volvo. They both are wearing their sunglasses and enjoying the lovely sunny day. Doris needs to stop at the bank. She leaves Henry sitting in the car and says, "Now Henry, you stay here, I have to run into the bank. Please do not leave the car, Dear."

Less than five minutes later, when Doris returned to the car, sure enough, there was no Henry in sight. Doris searched around the corner of the shopping mall, no sign of Henry.

"Oh Henry, where are you?" She then heard a response; she looked around the other corner, and there stood Henry, patting a dog. "Oh Henry, I was so worried; I asked you not to leave the car."

"I know," said Henry. "But I had to pee."

"Alright then," Doris said. "We will find a place for you to use the bathroom."

"It's OK," said Henry. "I already went."

Identify the phase that applies to the above story:
- ☐ Turmoil
- ☐ Transformation
- ☐ Transition
- ☐ Trust

Hint: see Chapter 13, "Where is Harry?" for what works and what doesn't.

Everybody's Looking for Someone

John lives at Daisy Park Manor nursing home. It is nearly dinner time and John is sitting in front of the nursing station, waiting for dinner to be served.

John is becoming restless and agitated. His hunger has made him tired of waiting. "Help, help," cries John. His voice becomes louder as well.

"What is it John? What's the matter?" asks Lily, his caregiver, worried that John might be having pain.

"I'm looking for Martha," responds John.

"Oh," says Lily. "Who is Martha?"

"She's cooking my dinner," says John. "Don't you know Martha? She's my wife, and I want to tell her I am hungry."

"Okay, John, I will tell Martha you are hungry. Tell me about Martha. How many years have you been married?" asks Lily.

"I love Martha very much. We've been together 62 years, can you call her for me?" asks John.

"Okay John, I will," responds Lily. Although this is a very busy time, Lily takes a moment to dial Martha's telephone number for John.

Dinner is now being served at Daisy Park Manor.

Identify the phase that applies to the above story:
- ☐ Turmoil
- ☐ Transformation
- ☐ Transition
- ☐ Trust

Hint: see Chapter 2, "Wheelchair Ballet" for what works and what doesn't.

Norman

*N*orman worked as a night watchman at the airport for over 40 years. Since being diagnosed with dementia, Norman has been a resident at Memory Care Lane. The routine here is very different for him, and Norman is having difficulty adjusting his "natural time clock." In fact, Norman gets up and wanders during the night. He doesn't use his call bell to call the nurses. One night, Norman climbed over the side rails of the bed to go to the bathroom. Norman's eyesight is failing, and the caregivers are worried that one of these nights he may fall and injure himself.

Norman's family has shared information about their Dad's employment history as a night watchman. The caregivers now welcome Norman to sit at the desk with them for a few hours on their night shift. Norman enjoys a cup of warm milk and a biscuit and shares many good stories of his night watchman duty at the airport. Seems he can't tell these stories enough times.

In the above situation, the nursing staff has worked together with the family member to set in place a realistic and much safer plan for Norman's care and sleeping routine. In fact, this challenge has become a sleeping solution.

Identify the phase that applies to the above story:
- ☐ Turmoil
- ☐ Transformation
- ☐ Transition
- ☐ Trust

Hint: see Chapter 3, "One Shoe On" for what works and what doesn't.

Hal

I was visiting with Hal one day and I noticed a photograph of a beautiful dog in his room.

"Hal, tell me about this dog," I said, thinking that he may have forgotten he had a dog at one time.

"Oh," says Hal. "That's my Chesapeake Retriever; he's a beautiful dog. In fact, he is my dog and always comes duck-hunting with me. Whenever I shoot the ducks, that dog goes swimming so far out in the swamp. He never misses the duck and brings it back to me. And when he does bring the duck back he is very happy about it, and his tail is wagging."

"That's great Hal," I said. "And what happens if one doesn't have a dog, and they go duck-hunting?"

"I guess they'll have to learn to swim," says Hal.

Stories like the above illustrate the need for reminiscence for the person with dementia. They love to tell stories. They love to talk. At times, some family members find visitation uncomfortable if their loved one is no longer communicating. In this instance, it is highly recommended to bring along to the visit something that is meaningful to the person. Examples include a keepsake or a photo that will "spark a memory."

Identify the phase that applies to the above story:

- ☐ Turmoil
- ☐ Transformation
- ☐ Transition
- ☐ Trust

Hint: see Chapter 18, "Bathing Sparky" for what works and what doesn't.

Vivienne

*V*ivienne has been a school teacher all her life. Now that she is diagnosed with dementia and is living in the special care unit at Tick Tock Manor, Vivienne thinks that we are all her pupils. She cannot go to sleep and her caregiver, Jenny, has brought the "Mary Had a Little Lamb" story for her to read.

"Oh, I remember this story," says Vivienne, as she reads to Jenny. "I used to read it to my pupils. I was a good teacher too, because I was so small, the students liked me." Jenny is surprised that Vivienne can still read.

In the above situation the caregiver spends some quality time with the person with dementia. This allows time for the person to reflect on past memories and provides an opportunity for sharing. Soon, Vivienne becomes sleepy and is more cooperative to settle for the night.

The very next morning, Vivienne has more stories to tell.

"I had to help my mother in the morning," says Vivienne. "There were nine of us children; I was in the middle, that is why I am so small. Now my kids are bigger than me."

This morning, Vivienne is telling Jenny about her childhood.

"I taught music to the children for many, many years," says Vivienne.

"How many pupils did you have Vivienne?" Jenny asks.

"Many, many pupils and they loved me. I taught them singing and dancing," she responded.

Vivienne has a big smile on her face.

Identify the phase that applies to the above story:
- ☐ Turmoil
- ☐ Transformation
- ☐ Transition
- ☐ Trust

Hint: see Chapter 7, "Flower Child" for what works and what doesn't.

Henry

*H*enry was a pilot for 36 years in the air force. He flew fighter jet planes. Henry has Alzheimer's disease. Today he wanders aimlessly, and cannot even navigate his way around his own home. He cannot remember being a pilot. Henry cannot even remember the names of his family members.

One day, his daughter had an inspiration. She made a memory box for her Dad. In it she placed some of Henry's treasured memories from when he was a pilot; some photos of Henry dressed smartly in uniform, two toy fighter jet planes, Henry's badges and medals, and some letters of recognition.

Now, Henry no longer wanders aimlessly around the house. He spends many hours reminiscing with his memories, with a big smile on his face.

Identify the phase that applies to the above story:
- ☐ Turmoil
- ☑ Transformation
- ☐ Transition
- ☐ Trust

Hint: see Chapter 6, "Hat Day at Daisy Park Manor" for what works and what doesn't.

Glossary

Alzheimer's disease
- irreversible dementia
- early-stage, middle-stage and late-stage
- documented by Dr. Alois Alzheimer in 1906
- plaques and tangles surround the neurons, hallmarking the disease

Activities of Daily Living (ADL's)
- the basic daily activities, including bathing, dressing, eating, sleeping, and toileting that the person with dementia may require assistance with

Activity
- provides enormous benefit for person with dementia
- alleviates boredom
- enhances self-esteem

Biographical information
- this information is obtained from the family who knows their loved one best.
- this knowledge empowers professional caregivers in care

Caregiver – family or professional
- the individual who works with the person with dementia through the phases of the journey, assisting to meet their activities of daily living that they no longer can manage on their own

Case-study approach
- a systematic way of looking at events, collecting data, analyzing information, and reporting the results

Catastrophic reaction
- disorganized behavior due to a threatening situation with which the person cannot cope

Creating contrast
- how to preserve the world as once remembered for persons with dementia

Dementia
- a global term describing the "broken brain"
- not a normal part of aging
- may be reversible or irreversible

Dementia journey
- there is one journey
- includes the phases of Turmoil, Transformation, Transition, and Trust

Dementia care journey
- person with dementia may be marching along on their own path
- caregiver is walking right beside the person with dementia, however, they each have their own reality

Living in the moment
- persons with dementia live totally in the moment
- they no longer have an attachment to anything material

Locked and keyed
- specially designed units for persons with Alzheimer's disease and related dementia to assure safety and prevent wandering

Multi-infarct dementia
- dementia resulting from multiple small strokes

Music therapy
- this therapeutic tool is very calming for persons with dementia

Normalization
- it is critical to provide some contrast to the daily routine. Activities do provide some normalization for persons with dementia

Person with dementia
- describes the individual who has Alzheimer's disease or related dementia

Personhood
- the sense of self; who this individual was before diagnosis

Range of motion exercise
- motivates the use of muscles
- this exercise can be active or passive

Respite
- caregiver gives self permission to take a break from caregiving

Resident
- this individual is now living in the nursing home or care facility

Shared lived experience
- case studies which depict the experience of living with the person with Alzheimer's disease and related dementia

Social isolation
- aloneness experienced by the individual and perceived as imposed by others and as a negative or threatened state

Strength based care
- focus on person's remaining strengths and what they still do really well. This empowers and enhances their present quality of life

About the Author

*G*wendolyn de Geest, RN, BSN, MA, is an educator and speaker in dementia care. She has been a professor at Vancouver Community College since 1986, where she currently teaches Home Support and Resident Care Attendant students, both in the classroom, nursing home, and special care unit settings.

Born in 1949, Gwendolyn grew up in Edmonton, Alberta, Canada. She was the spoiled daughter, born in between two brothers, and she quickly learned that she could cross a street by herself long before she was old enough to get married. She helped her family understand that the world wouldn't collapse if one went to bed with dirty feet. It was here in Edmonton that Gwendolyn earned her Nursing Diploma at The University of Alberta Hospital. During her training, she discovered that she was definitely a "high-touch and not a high-tech" type of nurse, as each and every time her nursing instructor entered the Operating Room, Gwendolyn would either drop or contaminate an instrument.

An amazing journey followed, and it would be more than twenty-five years, before Gwendolyn returned to learning, determined to achieve a BSN from the University of British Columbia.

In 2001, Gwendolyn completed three years of study and research at the University of Victoria Centre on Aging. The title of this project was, "The Relation Between the Perceived Role of Family and the Behavior of the Person With Dementia." This paper is published in the American Journal of Alzheimer's Disease (May/June, 2003). This study evoked so many themes and needs, both for the person afflicted with dementia, and their caregivers.

As a result of witnessing the joys and sorrows of these carers, Gwendolyn was moved to write The Living Dementia Approach that you are reading now. This work touches the lives of these individuals in a most intimate manner, allowing both their dignity and humanness to remain intact.

Gwendolyn lives in Vancouver, Canada with her husband and two children.

You can reach Gwendolyn at *gmdegeest@CruiseRespite.com*

ISBN 142511647-7

9 781425 116477